AEROBIC WEIGHT TRAINING

THE ATHLETE'S GUIDE TO IMPROVED SPORTS PERFORMANCE

FREDERICK C. HATFIELD, PH.D.

Contemporary Books, Inc.
Chicago

Library of Congress Cataloging in Publication Data

Hatfield, Frederick C.
  Aerobic weight training.

  Includes index.
  1. Weight lifting.   2. Physical fitness.
3. Physical education and training.   4. Aerobic
exercises.   I. Title.
GV546.H36   1983   613.7   83-7557
ISBN 0-8092-5533-2

Copyright © 1983 by Frederick C. Hatfield
All rights reserved
Published by Contemporary Books, Inc.
180 North Michigan Avenue, Chicago, Illinois 60601
Manufactured in the United States of America
Library of Congress Catalog Card Number: 83-7557
International Standard Book Number: 0-8092-5533-2

Published simultaneously in Canada by Beaverbooks, Ltd.
195 Allstate Parkway, Valleywood Business Park
Markham, Ontario L3R 4T8 Canada

Contents

Preface

The fitness boom in the United States is now past its first decade. That it is much more than a fad or passing fancy is supported by its age and the fact that the trend is ever upward. It has become a way of life for many—and it has become a means of prolonging life and improving the quality of life for all.

The surrogate father of the fitness boom is Dr. Ken Cooper, of *The New Aerobics* fame. In this famous book Dr. Cooper spelled out easy-to-follow guidelines for all to assess individual fitness levels. His method employed the concept that the heart was of vital importance in determining current fitness and in establishing a training regimen to improve physical condition. The exercise chosen by Dr. Cooper to develop cardiac efficiency was running. However, racquet sports, cycling, and swimming were also looked upon favorably by Cooper.

To be sure, running has advantages: Almost anyone can do it. It's relatively inexpensive. It can be done anywhere, even in your own living room, in place. And no equipment is required. These considerations are, at least in part, responsible for the tremendous popularity of Cooper's program. Literally millions of Americans are now running for their lives.

Running also has disadvantages. Orthopedic doctors the nation over are experiencing a boom in business which, they claim, is directly attributable to running injuries. In fact, many physicians reckon such running- or jogging-related injuries to be of epidemic proportions and have suggested numerous measures designed to decrease the risk of injury while running.

Running has often been viewed as some sort of panacea that will rid one of the ills of the world. Obesity, atherosclerosis, job-related productivity, and a host of other physical, social, and psychological manifestations of a sedentary and overindulgent lifestyle are claimed to be attenuated through running. Scientists involved in researching the benefits and risks of running in each of these disciplines have found that running may indeed *contribute* to general social, psychological, and physical well-being, but certainly not to the extent that other (sometimes more important) factors may be safely neglected.

The implications of this statement are immediately clear for the average fitness buff or person wishing to become a bit more fit. It takes much more than running to offset or reverse the harm done over years of physical neglect. The implications to athletes wishing to achieve a high degree of fitness for their respective sports, however, are not so clear. Coaches the world over persist in the antiquated belief that running is the only way to get into shape for sports. This is changing, but sports requiring high levels of endurance are still in the dark ages in their conditioning efforts. Sports such as basketball, wrestling, crew, soccer, and others that require aerobic as well as anaerobic conditioning are universally neglectful of what science has to offer in the general area of conditioning knowledge. The sports traditionally referred to as predominantly aerobic sports (e.g., long-distance swimming, long-distance running, and others) are now known to be very dependent on strength as well, particularly in the upper echelons of performance.

That running has limitations is clear. What is also clear is that very often, when running falls short of delivering desired fitness or conditioning goals, weight training should be implemented. Notwithstanding the tremendous benefit that can be derived from a well-thought-out running program, it is weight training that stands out as the single most versatile system ever devised for improving overall physical fitness.

This book is devoted to methods of improving aerobic fitness through weight training techniques. In the past, weight training techniques were limited to anaerobic fitness. Weight training is extremely well suited for improving strength, power, and muscular size. However, through the innovative application of old scientific principles, scientists discovered that weight training can also deliver considerable amounts of aerobic (endurance) benefits as well. In fact, such benefits surpass those that mere running can provide.

The methods and principles presented in this book will be of tremendous benefit to those wishing to truly maximize overall fitness—fitness beyond simple cardiovascular efficiency. And they will provide the serious athlete with new and more efficient means of conditioning that are vital to improving athletic performance.

Science marches on. What was once considered the ultimate in training technology is now considered a beneficial adjunct to new technology. Weight training offers much in the way of new technology, and when used in conjunction with traditional forms of aerobic training (running, etc.) the result is a better athlete and/or a more fit individual.

Before reading this book you may have to reevaluate what you once accepted as gospel. You will have to open your mind and realize that what you once accepted as fact is, in reality, fantasy. (For example, most fitness enthusiasts used to believe that weight training promoted inflexibility and made athletes muscle-bound.) What you once thought was the only way has become just a part of the whole program—often a rather insignificant part. Weight training is here to stay, and the thousands of new health spas and training facilities across the country emphasize this point. Weight training offers much in improving overall fitness, and millions of Americans have already discovered these benefits.

Acknowledgments

Sincere thanks are offered to my wife, Joy, for her love, understanding, encouragement, and patience throughout the writing of this manuscript. Also to my son, Freddy, and my daughter, Disa—they are the inspirations in my life.

A large measure of appreciation is also extended to Randy Wilson, my partner, who has always given me the drive and dedication I so often lacked in my writing.

1

Physiological Mechanisms of Endurance

INTRODUCTION

Generally, on-the-job performance will increase at a rate directly proportional to a person's acquisition of knowledge about the job. In sports, where a premium is placed on high performance levels, this is no less true. It has always seemed strange to me that athletes would blindly follow coaching advice or engage in the drudgery of repetitive drills day in and day out without really knowing why such practices were important. Then the thought struck me that a vast majority of coaches don't impart knowledge to their athletes. They simply tell them what to do. I have found that the primary reason that training and conditioning knowledge is not passed on is that the coaches themselves have precious little to give! The age of specialization gave birth to a new breed of coaches—the *strength and conditioning coach.* In many sports, and at all levels of competition, the head coach now limits his or her expertise to matters of technique and strategy and leaves the conditioning of the athletes to the strength and conditioning coach. This is prudent and wise.

But all of this specialization has made the lot of the athlete even tougher! Now, in order to improve his or her performance, the athlete is obliged to gain knowledge and understanding from

1

not one, but many, disciplines. That is, if it is still agreed that performance will indeed benefit from this increased wisdom. My guess is that it will.

What about the athlete who trains without the benefit of a coach? Indeed, what about the average fitness enthusiast who couldn't care less about sports or becoming an elite athlete? In both of these cases it becomes rather critical that a thorough knowledge of training principles be acquired. Without such knowledge the fitness buff and the athlete immediately place themselves at a very distinct disadvantage. Neither will ever achieve his or her potential. They haven't the knowledge to do so.

It is not enough to read a how-to book on achieving a greater level of fitness or conditioning. The underlying factors need to be understood as well. Each individual has different training problems, different goals, a different lifestyle, and a different level of motivation. So the cookbook approach that is espoused in most how-to books is going to be inadequate at best. But, armed with at least a working knowledge of the basic principles governing training, anyone can put together a reasonably sound and scientific training schedule.

This chapter is devoted to discussing the physiological factors underlying aerobic fitness, or endurance. Since many books have focused on running as the best method of achieving cardiovascular endurance, little will be said about running programs. Instead, the central theme of this book will be that weight training techniques stand out as being of great importance in any complete program for endurance training. This chapter will concentrate on those physiological factors that contribute to increased endurance capabilities. I believe that, with an understanding of the basic physiology of endurance, any athlete or fitness enthusiast can better devise a training program suited to his or her goals. And it will become clear that weight training is an extremely efficient and versatile means of doing so.

FACTORS DETERMINING ENDURANCE CAPABILITIES

From the standpoint of determining which specific factors contribute to endurance, three distinct types of endurance are identified. The first one is the one that most coaches and athletes alike generally refer to. It is *cardiovascular* endurance. The term *cardiovascular* refers to the efficiency with which blood can be transported to the body via the combined activity of the heart muscle and the circulatory system. Another related type of endurance is called *local muscular endurance.* Here the premium is placed on oxygen utilization and elimination of metabolic wastes from the cell—emphasis is placed on function at the cellular level rather than on the heart and blood vessels. The third type of endurance is called *strength endurance.* A muscle fatigues very quickly when maximum stress is placed on it. The ability to exert maximum muscular force time after time without appreciably diminishing in strength depends on both cardiovascular endurance and local muscular endurance. However, the emphasis is placed on strength and energy supplies within the muscle cell. All three are related to a great extent, but to maximize each, different types of training are required.

In sports the need for each type of endurance is immediately clear. Long-distance running and related activities require great cardiovascular endurance. Sports such as crew or wrestling require a high degree of local muscular endurance as well as a good level of cardiovascular endurance. Football, basketball, wrestling, and many other sports require explosive force to be applied repetitively. And if fatigue sets in, the amount of force will be reduced. It is vital that the athlete understand these different types of endurance and train appropriately for those that are required of him. Very often all three are required, and in order to maximize each, the athlete must use entirely different forms of training. There is no single method of training that will maximize all three.

While it is nice and neat to isolate the three types of endurance, it is nonetheless an artificial classification—the three are intricately interrelated, and compartmentalizing them is done only to facilitate understanding of each. Simply identifying those underlying physiological mechanisms responsible for endurance is not enough. Other factors weigh very heavily on one's endurance level. Two very important factors are *heredity* and *motivation.* These will be discussed as they become pertinent throughout the remainder of the book.

AEROBIC AND ANAEROBIC FITNESS

Understanding the nature of endurance as a component of physical fitness depends on first understanding some basic facts about how muscles work. In a very simplified sense muscles are turned off and on in much the same way that a car is accelerated and decelerated—more gas for greater power or less gas for reduced power output. But, at the cellular level, far more complex functions occur than merely increasing or decreasing effort.

During explosive types of physical activity (such as shot putting, high jumping, running short dashes, or competitive weight lifting) little or no oxygen is required in the cell. Instead, two so-called *fast energy substrates* are used. These fast energy substances are *adenosinetriphosphate* (ATP) and *creatine phosphate* (CP). When voluntary muscle contraction occurs, the brain sends a nervous impulse to the muscle involved. This nerve impulse in turn causes a breakdown of the ATP. The energy generated by the breakdown of the ATP is what causes muscles to contract. Without sufficient ATP there could be no muscle contraction. Within seconds after contraction begins, the stores of ATP are used up and a means of resynthesizing ATP must be found. That is where the CP comes in. In order to sustain muscular contraction for more than a few seconds, the CP is broken down, thereby releasing energy for the resynthesis of more ATP. Again, however, the stores of CP are quickly depleted, and now the muscle's "fuel" must be used to resynthesize additional CP. This fuel is called *glycogen*—it is the end product of digested food and is stored in columns alongside the muscle's contracting elements for easy access. As glycogen is broken down, it releases energy for the resynthesis of CP but also results in the buildup of *lactic acid*. If the muscle is called on to contract for periods greater than about 30 seconds, this lactic acid builds up to a point where the blood becomes too acidic, and muscle contraction halts. To understand this chain of events, try running as hard as you can for about 30 seconds and watch what happens to your legs. They will begin to feel like lead and will begin to fail to respond. It is the lactic acid that causes this diminution of effort. Highly trained athletes develop a greater tolerance to such lactate concentrations and are

FIGURE 1-1. Summary of the Steps Involved in the Anaerobic and Aerobic Pathways

1. Organic Phosphate $\rightarrow$ Inorganic Phosphate + Organic Phosphate + Energy
   ATP   P   ADP   E
   (Adenosine triphosphate)   (Phosphate)   (Adenosine diphosphate)

2. Organic Phosphate + Organic Phosphate $\rightarrow$ Organic Phosphate + Organic Mineral
   CP   ADP   ATP   C
   (Creatine Phosphate)   (Adenosine diphosphate)   (Adenosine triphosphate)   (Creatine)

3. Glycogen $\rightarrow$ Lactic Acid + Energy for resynthesis of CP
   (i.e., for putting "P" from step 1 and "C" from step 2 back together)

4. Organic Mineral + Inorganic Phosphate + Energy $\rightarrow$ Organic Phosphate
   C   P   E   CP

5. $1/5$ Lactic Acid + $O_2 \rightarrow CO_2 + H_2O$ + Energy for resynthesis of remainder of Lactic Acid

6. $4/5$ Lactic Acid + Energy (from step 5) + $O_2 \rightarrow$ Glycogen

Steps 1 through 4 are referred to as the *anaerobic pathway* because they do not involve the utilization of oxygen. Activities of an anaerobic nature include such sport events as jumping, throwing, shot put, competitive weight lifting, powerlifting, and sprints. Aerobic activities (the point at which the emphasis is on steps 5 and 6) include such activities as long-distance swimming, long-distance running and the like. Many (in fact, most) sports activities fall somewhere in between these two extremes and involve both aerobic and anaerobic pathways. Crew, wrestling, basketball, football, intermediate-distance swimming and running, and gymnastics are a few examples of sports requiring both (see Figure 1-2).

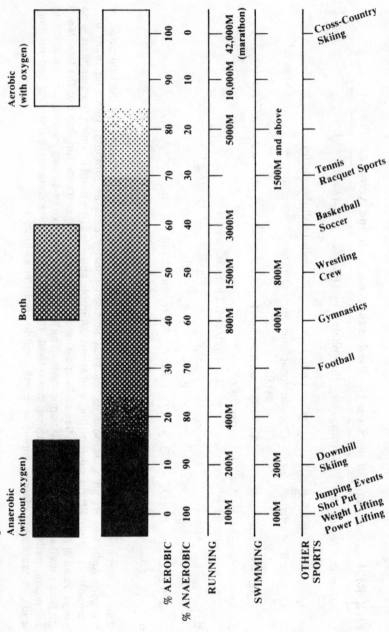

FIGURE 1-2. Relative amounts of Anaerobic versus Aerobic Fitness Required in Different Sport Activities

In the running and swimming events, researchers generally agree that at around three minutes (until about seven or eight minutes) there are relatively equal requirements in both the aerobic and anaerobic pathways for muscle energetics.

able to sustain maximum effort for longer periods of time than unfit individuals.

For muscle contraction to continue for periods greater than around 30 seconds, the amount of lactic acid building up in the muscle must be reduced. This is where the *anaerobic pathway* ends and the *aerobic pathway* begins. The term *anaerobic* means *without oxygen,* and the term *aerobic* means *with oxygen.* So, to continue muscle contraction, oxygen must be supplied to the muscle.

Oxygen is supplied to the muscle by binding to the hemoglobin in the blood and being physically transported to the site where it's needed. The efficiency with which this transport process takes place is one of the very important determinants of cardiovascular fitness. The oxygen combines with about one-fifth of the lactic acid, producing carbon dioxide, water, and energy. The CO_2 and H_2O are eliminated via normal breathing (the blood carries these metabolic wastes to the lungs where they are expelled). The energy given off in this chemical reaction is used to convert the remainder of the lactic acid and more oxygen to glycogen.

Now a complete loop has been formed. ATP is replenished, CP is replenished, lactic acid is combined with oxygen to produce more glycogen, and metabolic wastes are expelled. This chain of chemical events, when allowed to operate at this level, is called *steady state* work. This means that enough oxygen is being supplied to the muscle for work to continue indefinitely. Such steady state work is possible only when working at roughly 80 percent of one's maximum capacity or less. Of course, highly trained athletes are able to sustain work at loads considerably higher than can the average individual. This is true because of the greatly improved *oxygen transport* capabilities of the athlete and also because of the improved *oxygen utilization* capabilities that are promoted through training.

Should muscle contraction proceed at levels greater than roughly 80 percent of one's maximum capacity, an *oxygen debt* develops. *Oxygen debt* refers to the amount of oxygen it will take to allow that individual to return to normal (i.e., normal heart rate after the removal of metabolic wastes and the conversion of all of the lactic acid). Again, the ability to tolerate a greater oxygen debt is generally higher among trained athletes than among unfit individuals.

During this entire process the heart must pump more oxygenated blood to the muscle. Thus, there is an increase in *heart rate* and, with training, an increase in *stroke volume* as well. Heart rate is simply the number of times the heart beats per minute. Stroke volume is the amount of blood the heart pushes out with each beat. After exercise ceases the heart continues to beat fast but slows down as the oxygen debt is repaid.

We are now at a point where it is possible to describe what the term *endurance* really means. Functionally, it means the ability to do sustained work. But, to grasp the true significance of the term and to understand the rationale behind the many types of training programs designed to increase endurance, we need to progress beyond this meager definition.

DETERMINANTS OF CARDIOVASCULAR ENDURANCE

Figure 1–3 illustrates a very simplified overview of the determinants of cardiovascular fitness. As you will undoubtedly notice, a great emphasis is placed on gas transport as the primary determinant of one's ability to utilize oxygen. In the final analysis it can be said that, of the many factors involved in cardiovascular endurance, the most important by far is the ability to utilize the oxygen that is supplied to the muscle. Much more will be said about this fact throughout the remainder of the book, as the many types of training regimen are primarily concerned with improving the *max VO$_2$ uptake* (i.e., the maximum volume of oxygen that can be utilized by a muscle cell).

Because there is considerable overlap among cardiorespiratory endurance, local muscular endurance, and strength endurance in terms of the functional importance of these determinants of endurance, reviewing each from the standpoint of training effects is important. The extent to which the three types of endurance are interrelated will become quite clear, but so will the differences— the *differences* will show the way to appropriate training for each.

FIGURE 1-3. Determinants of Cardiovascular Endurance

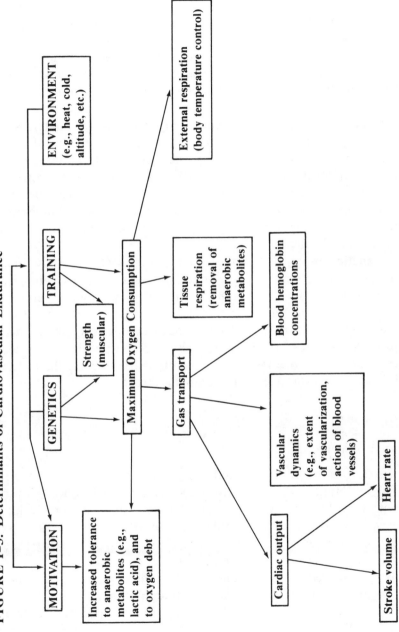

Genetics

Each person is born with an innate ceiling (or limit) beyond which endurance cannot improve. Many factors work in concert to establish this ceiling. Each of the factors listed in Figure 1–3 is, to a great extent, affected by genetic endowment. Since O_2 transport stands out as one of the most important determinants of cardiovascular endurance, and since it is limited by hereditary factors, it is probably the most important factor in terms of genetic capabilities as well. However, another factor of great importance is the amount of white versus red muscle fiber a person is born with. White muscle fiber is more conducive to explosive strength, whereas red muscle fiber is more conducive to muscular endurance. Later in this chapter red versus white muscle fiber and the importance of this factor in endurance training will be discussed fully.

Genetics impinge on practically all aspects of life. Body build, metabolic functions, muscular strength factors, and psychological factors all become important in predicting whether a person is capable of performing the tasks of any given sport or activity maximally. In some eastern European countries sports officials preselect athletes for the sports the children appear to be genetically endowed for. The factors mentioned above are the criteria by which such preselection attempts are made.

Environment

Extremes in environmental factors all influence performance. The endurance athlete's performance is generally reduced in very hot, very humid, or very cold weather and at extremely high elevations. However, if an athlete is used to high altitude and then performs at sea level, within a few days, his or her performance will increase. This is because at higher elevations the body adapts to the rarefied air by developing more hemoglobin to transport oxygen. Another factor, minute though it may be, is that at higher elevations less gravitational force acts on the athlete's body. Wind direction can, of course, become the deciding factor in an endurance race or sprint race—the stronger athlete will usually do better, all other factors being equal.

Motivation

All good coaches know the value of instilling motivation in their athletes. And all good athletes know the value of self-motivation. In an interesting experiment done to determine the effects of motivation on performance in an endurance task (riding a bicycle ergometer) a scientist by the name of Dr. J. H. Wilmore found that the imposition of a competitive situation facilitated performance. But his findings went much further than this perhaps obvious conclusion. He found that even though the subjects who performed in a competitive situation did significantly better at their bicycle-riding task, there were no significant differences (when compared to the noncompeting athletes) in heart rate, O_2 consumption, or maximum ventilation! Wilmore concluded that the supramaximal performances of the competing athletes were due to increased *anaerobic* capacity rather than *aerobic* capacity and that reduced psychological inhibitions caused these athletes to endure the effects of the anaerobic metabolites (i.e., lactic acid) better than their noncompeting counterparts.

Some interesting studies emanating from Springfield College support Wilmore's findings. Research findings indicated that beyond a certain level of max VO_2 uptake (approximately 75 ml of oxygen per kg of body weight per minute—see Figure 1-4) no advantage was gained by an athlete. Instead, such factors as *running technique, muscular strength,* and *motivation* were the keys to success.

Training

That a trained athlete will perform better than an untrained individual is self-evident. Inherited capabilities and motivation cannot produce a champion if there is no training involved. And for the average fitness enthusiast the effects of training are such that even the most unendowed individual will perform closer to his or her potential than will the raw beginner. Most of the remainder of this book will deal with training techniques and the physiological (and psychological) effects of training. Suffice it to say, for now, that genetically endowed individuals who are highly motivated will train more intensely and will have a far better chance of achieving championship status than those lacking in any one of these three areas.

FIGURE 1-4. Approximate Aerobic Capacities of Selected Groups of Athletes and Individuals (Continued)

Athlete or Sport	Sex	Average max VO₂ uptake
Nordic ski champions	M	70–85
Champion endurance athletes	M	80
	F	60–75
Marathon runners	M	75
Univ. cross-country runners	M	70
Cyclists (Canadian)	M	70
Orienteering team (Sweden)	M	58
Hockey team (Univ. Minn.)	M	55–65
Water polo and swimming	M	58
Pan Am teams in soccer, speed skating, boxing, and basketball	M	50–55
Highly trained middle-aged joggers	M	55
	F	50
Crew	M	48
Weight lifters	M	45
Gymnasts	M	42
Sedentary college students	M	42–46
	F	35
Sedentary middle-aged	M	35
	F	30
Post-heart attack patients	M&F	10–20

Max VO₂ uptake figures are expressed in milliliters of oxygen used in one minute per kilogram of body weight. It is interesting to compare these figures with the illustration of aerobic and anaerobic components of various sports presented in Figure 1-2. This group of figures was adapted from Krotee, M., and Hatfield, F. C., *The Theory and Practice of Physical Activity* (Dubuque: Kendall/Hunt Publishing Co., 1979), p. 24.

There is one more aspect of training that needs to be mentioned. That is the skill factor. As one's skill in any given activity or sport increases, so too does the efficiency factor. The more efficiently a person moves or performs a task, the less the metabolic cost will be. Lifting a heavy weight, for example, using back and arm muscles will tire an individual far more quickly than will the use of the legs. Similarly, rowing, hurdling, racquet sports, and most other skilled activities and sports have techniques that will tend, if performed properly, to reduce the energy expenditure, thereby enabling the individual to continue for greater periods of time. So skill or technique training is an essential phase of increasing one's ability to endure—such training should not be neglected. Even running has a skill component, and the skilled runner will almost always outlast the inefficient runner.

The Heart and Circulatory System

Figure 1–5 on page 14 illustrates the general construction of the heart and blood vessels. Proper training has a beneficial effect on both, as will be shown. The heart is a pump for the transport of blood through the circulatory system.

From the standpoint of the factors that limit human performance in endurance activities, the transport of oxygen to active muscles and the removal of carbon dioxide are of major importance. During extreme exercise of a prolonged nature the heart is called on to pump greater volumes of blood. *Cardiac output,* as it is called, is controlled by two factors: (1) heart rate, and (2) stroke volume. Cardiac output is the amount of blood ejected by the heart in one minute and it is usually expressed in liters per minute. The average-sized man, while resting, will move about five liters of blood per minute through the chambers of the heart. A highly trained athlete, on the other hand, may move as many as 42 liters per minute through the heart while exercising! So you can see the tremendous importance of having an efficient cardiovascular system in endurance events—the greater blood volume means more oxygenated blood sent to the working muscles and more efficient removal of metabolic wastes (CO_2). As was discussed earlier, gas transport is one of the most important determining factors of endurance.

Heart rate is the number of times a heart beats per minute, and stroke volume is the amount of blood ejected from the left ventricle of the heart with each beat. The physiological bases for increased heart rate are complex indeed and involve the interplay

FIGURE 1-5. The Heart and Circulatory System

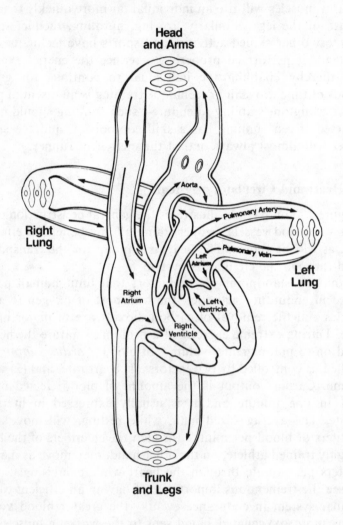

of receptors (proprioceptors and chemoreceptors) around the body, the brain (cerebral cortex), blood chemistry (carbon dioxide and lactate concentrations), and hormonal balances (adrenal gland). Heart rate is affected by factors such as age, sex, size, posture, food ingestion, body temperature, smoking, emotional state, and other environmental factors such as temperature and humidity.

The factors determining stroke volume are no less complex

than those determining heart rate. Stroke volume is generally thought to involve the interplay of four major factors: (1) effective blood pressure while the heart is being filled, (2) the distensibility (ability to stretch) of the left ventricle while it is being filled up with blood returning from the lungs, (3) the strength of the heart muscle during contraction (pushing the blood out of the left ventricle into the aorta for distribution around the body), and (4) general blood pressure in the circulatory system (arterial).

The effects of exercise on stroke volume are, from reviewing the factors listed above, quite clear. A stronger heart is capable of moving more blood. And lower blood pressure means that there will be less resistance against which the heart must push during ejection from the left ventricle into the aorta.

At this point it is necessary to review the factors involved in blood pressure. Doing so will give a clearer picture of how it affects stroke volume and (indirectly) heart rate. Figure 1-5 will

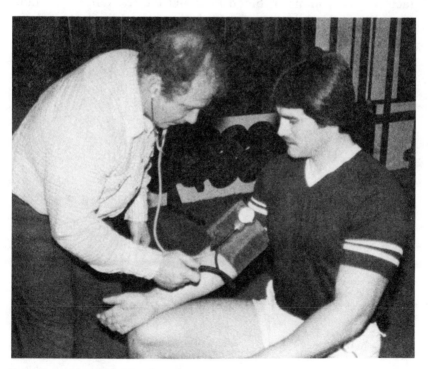

Scientist measuring blood pressure.

enhance understanding of the factors discussed above as well as the following discussion of blood pressure.

The terms *systolic* and *diastolic* are used in reference to blood pressure. In measuring blood pressure, a *sphygmomanometer* is used. The cuff of this device is applied to the upper arm and filled with air, thereby closing the brachial artery that runs down the arm. As air is slowly released from the cuff, the sound the blood makes is monitored through the use of a *stethoscope*. When the brachial artery is allowed to open sufficiently for blood to pass through, thereby measuring (indirectly) the force of a heart beat, a *systolic* reading is taken. When air is further released from the cuff, and all sounds disappear, a *diastolic* reading is taken. Thus, *systole* refers to the strength of the heart beat, whereas *diastole* refers to the pressure inside the artery during the resting phase of the heart.

To illustrate the interplay among stroke volume, heart rate, and blood pressure, remember that blood pressure depends on two factors—the volume of blood flow and the resistance it encounters. Blood flow, we have found, is determined by stroke volume and heart rate. However, the extent of resistance is determined by the tonus of the arterial muscles and any plaque buildup on the walls of the arteries (plaque buildup to any restrictive degree is referred to as *atherosclerosis* and is one of the most prevalent coronary diseases).

Healthy versus Atherosclerotic Arteries.

| Normal Artery | Fatty Deposits in Vessel Wall | Plugged Artery with Fatty Deposits and Clot |

DETERMINANTS OF LOCAL MUSCULAR ENDURANCE

As we have already noted, muscular endurance differs from cardiovascular endurance in that emphasis is placed on function at the cellular level rather than on the entire muscular system of the body. In other words, local muscular endurance relates to specific muscles' ability to perform sustained work, whereas cardiovascular endurance becomes paramount when no single muscle is being stressed but the work load is being distributed throughout the entire body (as in long-distance swimming or running).

The physical dynamics of these two types of endurance share many components, but there are important differences as well—it is the differences that determine the specific form of training that must be adopted to maximize performance in each. For example, local muscular endurance is limited by energy supply, muscular strength, and the extensiveness of the vascular bed (capillaries) in the working muscle. However, in general endurance (cardiovascular endurance) the outer limits of performance are regulated by the central systems of circulation, heat dissipation, respiration, and other homeostatic mechanisms that regulate total bodily function (see Figure 1-6).

Energy Supply

Anaerobic and aerobic pathways of muscular energetics have been discussed. Refer back to Figure 1-1, and you will see that the energy for muscular contraction is derived from the breakdown of ATP, CP, and glycogen. These, then, are the cell's sources of energy. Both ATP and CP are resynthesized to enable the cell to maintain contraction. ATP, as we have already seen, is resynthesized by the breakdown of CP. However, as CP stores are depleted, glycogen must be broken down to effect resynthesis. The breakdown of glycogen produces lactic acid. As the pH of the cellular fluid decreases (i.e., becomes more acidic) as a result of increasing lactate concentrations, the cell's ability to contract diminishes. Scientists believe that the lowered pH within the cell causes an inactivation of the myofibrillar protein *troponin*. The *myofibrillar elements* are the actual contractile units of a muscle cell, and the inactivation of these elements will cause the cell to stop working.

Ordinarily, during aerobic work, oxygen is supplied to the cell to assist in ridding the cell of the lactic acid. However, when a muscle contracts very strongly, and for a sustained period of time, blood cannot get to the cell because the strong contraction occludes circulation. When a muscle contracts, it shortens and bulges at its midpoint. This bulging physically crimps or pinches the tiny capillaries shut, thereby preventing blood from flowing to the site of fatigue.

Extent of Muscle Vascularity

One of the most important effects of training for muscular endurance is the improved vascularity of the muscle. For example, E. G. Martin and his co-workers showed as far back as 1932 that there were only half as many open capillaries in a muscle at rest as when that muscle was working. Thus, one important training effect is believed to be that some of these generally dormant capillaries open and remain open, thereby improving blood flow.

Improved vascularity around active muscle tissue has the net effect of increasing blood flow to the working muscle. This, in turn, will enable the muscle to get the additional oxygen that it needs to reduce the concentration of lactic acid in the muscle cell. As we have seen, lactic acid will change the pH of the cell's fluids, thereby causing a cessation of muscle contraction.

If the muscle is required to hold a very strong contraction for too long, blood flow is severely retarded owing to capillary occlusion. However, the existence of greater numbers of capillaries will decrease the pressure somewhat, since there are more avenues for blood to flow through. This is particularly true at work loads lower than around 60 percent of maximum effort.

It appears that the key to maintaining adequate blood flow through a working muscle is to engage in submaximal effort of a rhythmic (as opposed to static) nature. The intermittent rest pauses will permit momentary blood flow increases, thereby decreasing lactate levels in the cell. However, of equal significance is the ability of the muscle to contract repeatedly with *maximum* exertion. This is called *strength endurance*.

FIGURE 1-6. Determinants of Muscular Endurance and Strength Endurance

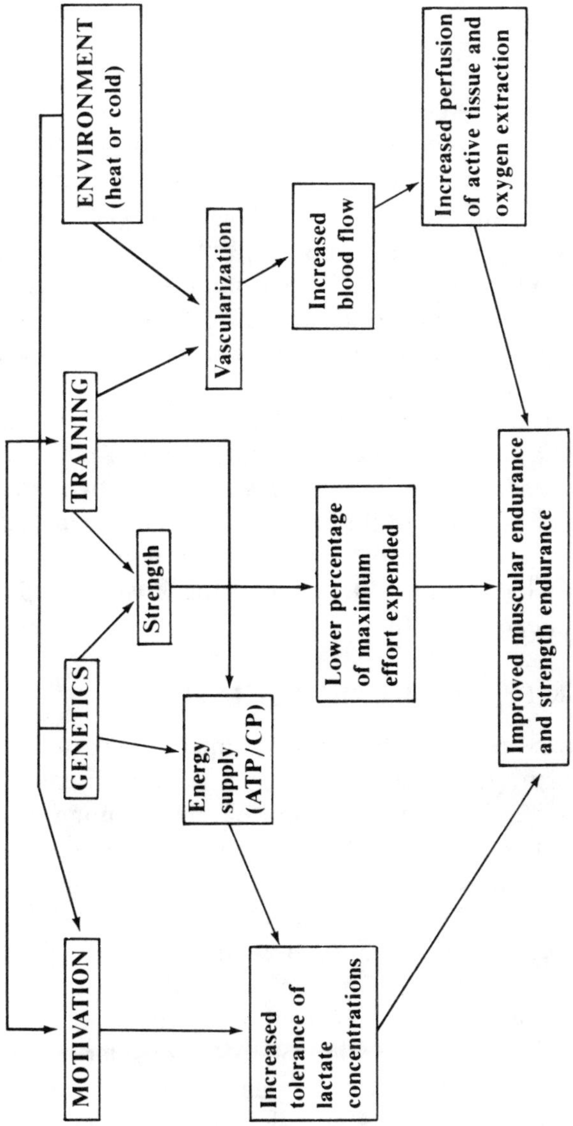

Muscular Strength

Scientists differentiate between *absolute* endurance and *relative* endurance. In the real world of sport performance absolute endurance is the most important. To illustrate the difference between the two, consider the example of two men having to hold a 25-pound weight at arms' length for as long as possible. One man weighs 150 pounds, and the other weighs 250 pounds. If we can assume that the big man is the stronger, which of the two will hold the weight at arms' length the longest? Of course, the stronger man will. Thus, the stronger man is said to have greater absolute endurance. Now, if each man were required to hold at arms' length a weight that was equal to a certain percentage of their respective body weights, no such advantage would be gained by the bigger man. Both men would, in this instance, have an equal chance of winning the contest, and the winner would be assumed to possess a greater amount of relative endurance.

The same analogy can be drawn using two men of equal weight. The stronger of the two will invariably win such a contest. Strength, then, is a very important component of muscular endurance. The stronger the muscle, the lower the percentage of maximum exertion it has to expend on any given task.

MUSCLE TYPE: A GENETIC TRAIT

Each person is born with many inherited characteristics. Body type, appearance, predispositions to certain diseases, and many other traits are given to us by our parents. Among these inherited characteristics the nature of muscle tissue is extremely important in setting the absolute limits of human performance. There are, of course, others that are important—a few, such as one's ability to utilize oxygen, have already been discussed. Each individual is born with an inherited ratio of three different types of muscle fiber, each of which has different capabilities.

To simplify the description of each, consider the last time you ate chicken. Chicken is either dark meat or white meat. The chicken's breast is white muscle, and for a very good reason. *White muscle fiber* has a greater *twitch* capacity. That means that the muscle twitches more times per second, thereby increasing the overall strength of contraction. However, because it has very few *mitochondria,* as well as a relatively poor blood supply (fewer capillaries), white muscle fiber has low endurance. Mitochondria are tiny subunits of a muscle cell that assist in the utilization of oxygen as well as in the manufacture of ATP. On the other hand, a chicken's legs are dark meat—or, in more scientific terms, *red muscle fiber.* Such muscle fiber has greater endurance capabilities because of the presence of more capillaries and mitochondria but does not have as extensive a nerve supply as does white muscle fiber. The relatively poorer nerve supply makes the strength of a red muscle cell's contraction somewhat less than that of white muscle cells.

What does this tell us about chickens? Chickens are ground birds. They need explosively powerful wing action (breast muscles) to get their fat bodies out of harm's way, but on the other hand never have to engage in long-distance flights. Their legs need good endurance to carry those fat bodies around all day (thus the red muscle fiber). (The breast muscles of a duck are all red fiber, or dark meat, thereby giving them great endurance for the long flights they undertake each season.)

Human muscles have similar differentiation. White muscle cells have greater strength and explosiveness but poorer endurance, and red muscle cells have just the opposite. Also, the red and white fibers are spread out rather than all in one muscle. Humans also have *intermediate muscle fibers.* These intermediate muscle fibers have good strength of contraction as well as good endurance capabilities.

The significance of determining a person's muscle fiber type lies not so much in establishing an appropriate training program as in establishing his or her innate capabilities for achieving excellence in various sports. For example, a person who is born with predominantly red muscle fiber has virtually no hope of ever becoming a great weight lifter, shot-putter, sprinter, high jumper, or discus thrower—these sports require great explosive strength (anaerobic capabilities). On the other hand, the same person stands a much better chance of becoming a great marathon runner or Nordic skier—sports requiring great endurance.

Exercise scientists have taken muscle biopsies (small samples of muscle) from many groups of champion athletes and have found this fact of genetic predisposition to be true. The great majority of sports require both aerobic and anaerobic excellence, however, and the person endowed with an equal amount of red and white muscle fibers tends toward excellence in these sports (refer back to Figure 1-2).

While training cannot alter the inherited ratio of white versus red muscle fiber, it can slightly alter the functional capabilities of each. Red muscle fiber can become stronger, and white muscle fiber can become more enduring through proper training procedures. The intermediate fibers also become more enduring or stronger with proper training. However, regardless of one's red-/white muscle fiber ratio, increasing either cardiovascular endurance or local muscular endurance will involve training for strength as well as endurance. Chapter 2 is devoted to methods of training for each.

SUMMARY

There is no easy way to describe the underlying physiology of endurance. The complexity of the subject prohibits a simplistic definition. However, it is vitally important that any athlete, coach, or fitness enthusiast understand at least the basic dynamics of aerobic fitness if the goal is to maximize training efficiency and training results.

This chapter identified the determinants of three interrelated types of endurance: (1) cardiovascular endurance, (2) local muscular endurance, and (3) strength endurance. Cardiovascular endurance was seen to be largely dependent on maximizing oxygen utilization. The key element in max VO_2 uptake is cardiac output and gas (oxygen) transport. Local muscular endurance, on the other hand, focuses on cellular function—available fast energy substrate (ATP and CP) and the extensiveness of the capillary bed in the working muscle were seen to be of critical concern. The ability to exert maximum force time after time is referred to as *strength endurance*. While both local muscular endurance and cardiovascular endurance are necessary for great strength endurance, of primary concern are the factors involved in local muscular endurance, with emphasis on muscular strength and energy supplies.

Factors such as motivation, genetic traits, training, and environmental conditions play an important part in setting the ceiling for aerobic capabilities. In the following chapter the physiological factors discussed in Chapter 1 are used to establish training principles, and in Chapter 3 these principles are systematically applied to training methods for improving on the three types of endurance.

2

The Basic Principles of Conditioning

INTRODUCTION

Getting in shape means different things to different people. To the fitness enthusiast it means improving on general fitness—*all* of the various components of fitness. To athletes it means improving on those components of fitness that are essential to their particular sports. To some it may simply mean flattening the tummy or losing weight. To others it may involve improving on cardiovascular efficiency. Yet others may wish to rehabilitate themselves after periods of immobilization (as after having a cast removed from a limb), heart attack, or other injuries or surgery.

Regardless of one's motives, and regardless of the means by which one strives to get into shape, one commonality underlies all forms of exercise. It is *stress.* Whether you skip rope, jog, lift weights, ride a bicycle, swim, or play sports, if you want to improve on any aspect of fitness, you must put your body under stress. If any of the various forms of exercise are performed at a level under (an average of) 60 percent of your maximum capacity, your body will not adapt to the stress—the stress will not be of sufficient intensity for an adaptive process to be forced to occur. Furthermore, if the type of stress is not of a rather exact nature, depending on which component of fitness you strive to achieve, the desired level of fitness will not be attained.

24

For example, all your life you have been walking and running around on your two legs. No amount of additional walking and running (of the same intensity as that practiced over your lifetime) will force the legs to become stronger, bigger, or more enduring. In order to force an adaptive process to occur in your legs, you will have to apply stress at a level in excess of what you have been used to—that is, the level to which your legs have already adapted.

These relatively simple facts have been known for some time in the world of exercise. But it wasn't until all of the various and complex physiological factors underlying each of the components of fitness were discovered that exercise scientists were able to put together all of the various principles governing efficient training. This chapter will explore these basic principles and in so doing will refer back to the information presented in Chapter 1 relating to the physiology of muscles at work.

FIGURE 2-1. The Basic Principles of Conditioning

1. *The Overload Principle:* As adaptation to stress occurs, progressively increasing resistance must be applied to ensure continued adaptation.
2. *The Isolation Principle:* Overload will best be served if a muscle is isolated from all others during any given exercise. The weakest muscle of a working group will derive the most benefit while the others that are working submaximally will receive little or no benefit.
3. *The SAID (Specific Adaptation to Imposed Demands) Principle:* The demands that are imposed on a muscle will force very specific processes of adaptation to occur. Only those components of a cell that are stressed (overloaded) will adapt.
4. *The Simulation Principle:* An activity's movement patterns must be duplicated against resistance to maximize facilitation of the motor learning process (i.e., the acquisition of the skill). Further, in order that the increases in size, strength, or endurance of a muscle resulting from training be facilitative of a skilled movement (rather than disruptive), that skill must be practiced during the training period.
5. *The Deinhibition Principle:* With overload, the inhibitory mechanisms that limit the extent of muscular exertion can be altered such that greater muscular force can be applied before the inhibitory response is elicited.

THE FIVE BASIC PRINCIPLES

There are five basic principles of conditioning—these five govern literally all methods of exercise. These principles determine the kinds of adaptive processes that will occur by manipulating the *frequency, intensity,* and *duration* of stress application to the muscles. You will see that the terms *application of stress* and *exercise* are synonymous.

Figure 2–1 lists the five basic principles of conditioning. Taken collectively, they encompass the total of man's knowledge about the effects of applying stress to the human body in such a way that constructive adaptation occurs.

The Overload Principle

There are many different ways to overload a muscle, and the exact nature of the method chosen will ultimately determine the adaptive response. For example, you can increase the amount of weight being used, thereby effectively increasing the overload on the muscles. Or, alternatively, the number of repetitions or sets of repetitions can be increased. The length of each workout can be increased, as can the number of workouts per week. The rest periods between each set can be reduced, and the speed with which each set is performed can be increased. Whichever method of overload you choose, bear in mind that the response to one method may be entirely different from the response to another. More will be said on this point later in this chapter when the SAID principle is discussed.

Overloading the muscle can be accomplished in varying degrees of severity. Applying stress on the muscle to an extent just slightly more than that muscle is used to is considered mild overload. The continuum progresses up to severe overload, wherein extremely heavy weights are used for the required number of repetitions. This is an important point, for it is the required number of repetitions that the SAID principle keys on in order to elicit the desired adaptive response to stress. As a general rule, healthy individuals should always strive to overload as severely as possible within these guidelines. Beginners, children, and older folks (some of whom may be cardiac patients or in a high-risk category insofar as the heart function is concerned) should restrict the level of overload to the lower end of the continuum—keep it mild. For example, just the act of walking up a flight of stairs may constitute considerable overload for the cardiac patient or the patient just recovering from injury or surgery.

In aerobic forms of weight training, where endurance is the objective, the number of repetitions the trainee will be required to perform will almost always be more than 15. The average healthy individual can generally perform this number of repetitions with a weight that is equivalent to at least 70 percent of his or her maximum for that exercise. With training, you will generally notice that 15 repetitions can be performed rather easily with 70 percent of your maximum, and you will have to increase your effort to closer to 80 percent of your maximum. That is, if you could perform only one repetition with 100 pounds, you will likely be able to perform 15 repetitions with between 70 and 80 pounds.

The key to determining whether you are overloading a muscle correctly is that the last repetition in each set you perform should be a near-maximum effort. That is, if you were performing five sets of 15 repetitions in any given exercise, and your maximum for one repetition was 100 pounds, your efforts would be something like this:

> 1st set: 15 repetitions with 80 pounds
> 2nd set: 15 repetitions with 80 pounds
> 3rd set: 15 repetitions with 75 pounds
> 4th set: 15 repetitions with 70 pounds
> 5th set: 15 repetitions with 60 pounds

The near failure to complete the last set of 15 repetitions with 60 pounds would tell you that you're overloading correctly. The dropoff in the amount of weight being used in each set will, of course, be due to fatigue.

While the amount of weight is of critical importance to the endurance athlete striving to achieve maximum overload, so is the rate at which the heart is beating. One of the crucial aspects of proper overload in cardiovascular endurance training is that the heart rate be kept above 60 percent of its maximum. The general rule of thumb in determining your maximum heart rate is to subtract your age from 220. Thus, for a 25-year-old athlete, the maximum heart rate will be 195 beats per minute, and 60 percent will be 117 beats per minute. If the heart is not working at or above this rate, no appreciable cardiovascular benefit will be derived from the exercise. Most exercise physiologists recommend that healthy athletes try to maintain at least 80 percent of their maximum heart rate for at least 20 minutes in each workout in order to maximize the cardiovascular benefit derived.

It used to be said that weight training was not beneficial to the heart because it did not provide the athlete with a means of keeping the heart rate at this prescribed level for a sufficient length of time. You will discover, however, that there are many different forms of weight training, and considerable cardiovascular benefit can be derived from proper weight training. And, of course, if your goal is to improve local muscular endurance or strength endurance, the heart rate factor no longer is critical, and other means of weight training become more appropriate.

Besides the amount of weight and one's heart rate, there are other manifestations of overload that will be of interest to the endurance athlete. For example, lactate concentrations within the cell, blood pressure during the performance of an exercise, the speed of limb movement during exercise, the amount of stress placed on connective tissue in the muscles and joints, and other factors all constitute overload in one way or another. And each form of overload must be maximized in order to elicit the desired adaptive response. Going beyond maximal levels, however, can prompt a maladaptive response in some instances.

To illustrate this point, take a look at a laborer's hands. Callus has formed from the continual friction against rough surfaces his hands have been in contact with. This is an example of an appropriate and beneficial adaptive response to stress. However, if the friction against the same rough surface were applied too quickly or too strenuously, blisters would have appeared rather than calluses. This, of course, would be an example of a maladaptive response. The human body works that way—it adapts to stress. Finding the most efficient way to apply stress such that a desired adaptive response is forced to occur is the exercise physiologist's job and the job of any athlete wishing to improve his or her chances of winning.

FIGURE 2-2. The Numbers of Repetitions the Trainee Should Perform at Various Intensities.

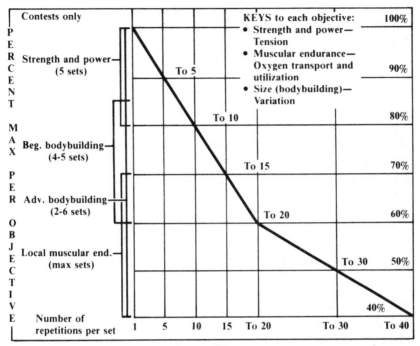

The SAID Principle

Until now, I have been talking about overload and the proper ways of applying it. In actuality, the SAID principle speaks to this as well. *SAID* stands for *specific adaptation to imposed demands*. In other words, the body will adapt to the demands imposed on it in highly specific ways. Figure 2-2 illustrates this point. Notice that the heavier the weight you use, the fewer the repetitions you can perform. Also, with heavier weights the emphasis shifts toward the strength and power end of the scale, whereas with lighter weights the emphasis is on endurance.

This differentiation of adaptive responses occurs because heavier weights performed for few repetitions keys on the anaerobic pathway of muscle energetics, whereas higher numbers of repetitions force the muscle cell to utilize oxygen in order to remove the waste products building up there. Chapter 1 contains a full explanation of the differences between anaerobic and aerobic forms of exercise, and at this point it may prove helpful to review that discussion. It is clear that different aspects of the muscle cell are being stressed in aerobic training than in anaerobic training, and the adaptive response that will be forced to occur in the cell will also be different.

Endurance athletes need to remember (from Chapter 1) that strength is important from the standpoint of improving on both absolute and relative endurance. In most cases, then, strength training as well as endurance training with weights will be called for. Each form of training is unique, and the outcomes will also be unique—no single method of training will suffice if excellence is your goal.

The Isolation Principle

As stated in Figure 2-1, the ability to impose maximum overload on a muscle will generally be facilitated if you allow that muscle to work without the assistance of other muscles. You must attempt to isolate it. Choosing the appropriate piece of weight training equipment and using it properly is the best insurance for this. Because the human musculoskeletal system is complex, however, it often becomes impossible to achieve total isolation of certain muscles. When this is evident you must at least try to make the muscle you are interested in developing do the bulk of the work to an extent that adaptive overload is applied. This can be accomplished only if there are no other muscles working that are stronger than the muscle you are interested in. In other words, try to make the target muscle the weakest in the link. Then it will feel the greatest impact of the applied stress. The other (stronger) muscles will generally not receive sufficient overload to force them to adapt to greater size, strength, or endurance. In the real world of sport, however, this will rarely become a problem because all one really has to do is to simulate the movement of his or her sport against sufficient resistance to force an adaptive response.

Simulation Principle

During the conduct of skilled movements in sport there is a complex interplay among one's sensory organs, brain, and muscles. Highly coordinated activities depend very much on sensory input. As a skill becomes automatic—or habit—the motor pathways from the brain to the muscle are ingrained. There are two ways in the weight training field to accomplish such facilitation of motor pathways. The first (and most frequently used) is to train with weights in the correct fashion and to practice the skills of the sport separately. In such training, size, strength or power, and muscular endurance are achieved. Then, to accommodate such increases to the new body that has been developed, the skills are practiced concurrently in order to keep the motor pathways required in the skills finely tuned.

The second way is to practice the skill applying greater-than-normal resistance; for example, shot putting with a 20-pound shot instead of the conventional 16-pound shot or running up hills with a heavy backpack instead of doing flat-surface running. Many such examples exist, and the effectiveness of such training has become self-evident over the years. However, one must be sure that the skill is practiced rather precisely in this form of weight training, because the increased weight could cause the movement pattern to be altered slightly. Also, fatigue could cause the same kind of movement alteration, the net result being a decrement in skill level rather than a facilitation of the correct motor pathways. Practiced correctly, however, both of these adjunctive forms of weight training can help you improve or maintain a high level of skill during the weight training process.

The Deinhibition Principle

Located at the ends of muscles, where the tendons begin, is a tiny sensory organ called the *Golgi tendon organ*. This tiny mechanism picks up sensations of stretching when muscle contraction becomes too great. The brain is alerted to this potentially dangerous situation and sends an inhibitory message back to the contracting muscle to shut down. This process is referred to as an *inhibitory feedback loop* and is designed to be a protective mechanism—it prevents one from literally pulling the muscles out of the bone or tearing other connective tissues. However, the point at which the inhibitory message is sent is generally a very conservative distance away from the point at which such tissue rupture would occur. Training (particularly weight training) tends to cause a slight retreat of the shutdown point, closer to the rupture point. This allows greater strength to be exerted by the muscle before the inhibitory message is sent. Using extremely heavy weights in training, as well as controlled jerky movements, can promote this shift in excitation thresholds (the point at which shutdown occurs) of Golgi tendon organs.

The excitation threshold is seen by many exercise scientists as the single most important factor in determining the level of strength of a muscle, since it is very often the weak link among the many factors determining strength. Most athletes engaging in endurance-type sports have little to do with maximum strength output, so this principle is of little importance to them. However, for the vast majority of athletes, their sports require considerable levels of both strength and endurance. This principle, then, is of considerable importance to them. This is especially true in light of the fact that strength is seen as an important factor in absolute endurance (see Chapter 1).

SUMMARY

The interrelatedness of the five principles of conditioning is apparent when one views the many methods there are of over-loading the organism. There are methods of overloading the heart, the circulatory system, the Golgi tendon organs, the aerobic functions and anaerobic functions of muscle cells, and even the motor pathways involved in complex sport skills. Figure 2–3 lists many of the commonly used methods of overload and the corresponding outcome(s) of each.

Without overload, there can be no adaptation. And the greater the overload (short of injury), the better—the body will adapt faster and to a greater degree with severe overload than with mild overload.

These five principles govern virtually all forms of exercise.

**FIGURE 2-3. Methods of Overload and
Their Corresponding Effects**

Overload Method	*Result*
Increase the weight	Strength
Increase the repetitions	Muscular endurance
Increase the movement speed of heavy weights	Explosive power
Increase the heart rate	Cardiovascular endurance
Increase the duration of effort per rep	Capillarization (vascularity) and strength
Increase the number of maximum efforts per set and per workout	Strength endurance and strength
Minimize the rest between sets	Cardiovascular endurance or muscular endurance
Increase the number of exercises per day	Cardiovascular endurance or muscular endurance
Increase the number of training sessions per week	Cardiovascular endurance or muscular endurance
Increase the tension and/or explosiveness of the movements	Strength, power, and deinhibition of Golgi tendon organ

While certain forms of exercise may prove better than others in achieving a specific training goal, weight training stands out as being the single most versatile method of achieving overall conditioning. Why? Simply because through weight training it is easier to apply the correct form of overload for the great majority of training goals.

Chapters 1 and 2 have provided the most important theoretical points needed in constructing a truly effective conditioning program for your sport. In Chapter 3 the various systems of training will be outlined. The physiological facts presented in Chapter 1, together with the basic principles presented in this chapter, are the cornerstones of all of the systems of training presented in Chapter 3. And the better these facts and principles are understood, the more efficient will be your training efforts—and the higher will be your athletic achievements.

FIGURE 2-4. Prescribed Methods of Overloading for Strength, Power, Muscular Size, and Endurance

Variable	Power	Strength	Size	Muscular Endurance
Percentage of maximum weight	85–95	75–90	60–90	50–80
Duration per set (seconds)	5	10	5–25	25–75
Repetitions per set	4–6	6–10	6–25	15–40
Sets per exercise	4–5	5–6	3–4	3–4
Rest between sets (minutes)	5–7	5–7	2–7	2
Speed per repetition	maximum	moderate to slow	variable	slow
Workouts per week	1–2	2–3	2–3	7–14
Exercises per muscle	1	1–2	2–3	1
Key to each objective	explosiveness	tension	variation	oxygen transport and oxygen utilization

3

Systems of Training for the Endurance Athlete

INTRODUCTION

In Chapters 1 and 2 the fact that endurance athletes require a fair amount of strength as well as muscular endurance and cardiovascular endurance became evident. At the very highest levels of competition in endurance sports the determinant of success was not one's max VO_2 uptake—research studies have shown that max VO_2 uptake capacity beyond approximately 75 milliliters of oxygen per minute for each kilogram of body weight was not of major significance in predicting success in long-distance running. Rather, such factors as muscular strength, technique (skill), and motivation became the critical factors.

This is a point that the average endurance athlete has traditionally overlooked. While running and related forms of training continue to stand out as the most efficient forms of endurance training (heart function is, after all, of major importance in achieving a high max VO_2 uptake level), strength, skill, motivation, and muscular endurance cannot be neglected. This point is self-evident if excellence is one's objective.

The scope of this book does not permit in-depth coverage of training information related to skill, running programs, or motivational techniques. These are areas which a good coach or another few volumes of writing must contend with. In this book methods of weight training are presented that will, perhaps more efficiently than any other methods known to science, instruct athletes and fitness enthusiasts alike in the best methods of achieving strength and muscular endurance. Also, excellent weight training methods of achieving cardiovascular efficiency are presented. Because there are so many different ways of manipulating the application of overload on the human body in weight training, this kind of training stands out as the most efficient and versatile form of training ever devised. Running for runners, swimming for swimmers, skiing for skiers, and wrestling for wrestlers will, of course, remain the single most important developmental activity for these respective classes of athletes. But properly applied weight training is, by all reasoning, an important adjunctive training tool for any athlete aspiring to championship status. And it is also an important training tool for the fitness enthusiast aspiring to become as fit as possible.

The systems of training presented in this chapter all adhere, in strict fashion, to the basic principles of conditioning presented in Chapters 1 and 2. There are as many systems of training as there are individuals training, so use them as guides rather than dogma. Individual differences in goals, sport endeavors, and lifestyle; availability of proper equipment, time, and training partners; and a host of other factors may require adapting any one of these systems to fit any given need. There is no best system written here—only guidelines. There is no gospel to which the athlete religiously clings—but there is a group of basic principles.

Over the years four systems have proven excellent for developing strength, muscular endurance, and cardiovascular endurance. The exact degree to which one reaches these three objectives depends on the way in which the overload factors are manipulated. The four systems are: (1) circuit training, (2) interval training, (3) peripheral heart action training, and (4) parcourse training. All four have offshoots that, when designed with the basic principles in mind, can be as good as the parent systems.

Many very refined and sophisticated systems of training exist that will improve power, strength, and size to an extent far greater than the four covered here. Since the goal of the endurance athlete is generally *endurance,* however, they are not included. (If power, strength, and size are your goals, the following two books are excellent sources of information: *The Complete Guide to Power Training* by F. C. Hatfield [New Orleans: Fitness Systems, 1982]; and *Toning Your Body* by S. Bentley and F. C. Hatfield [Piscataway, NJ: New Century Publishers, 1982].) All four systems covered here have the capacity to deliver relatively high levels of strength, local muscular endurance, and cardiovascular endurance, but the exact method used and exercises performed depend entirely on one's goals, sport endeavor, current state of fitness, and—for the competing athlete—position in the yearly training and competition cycle. In-season training and off-season training differ because the goals of each differ.

CYCLICAL TRAINING

The goal of any athlete's training during the competitive season is to maximize his or her performance at the contest. A fine line exists between training too much or too heavily and not training enough. Overtraining is by far the most common error of athletes in practically all sports. Proper peaking techniques must be used to ensure that one's performance level is at its highest point at the contest. Unfortunately, most athletes get anxious and train excessively hard in the premeet period, and they peak their bodies and psychological readiness days and even weeks prior to the contest. The result is, of course, lowered performance levels on the day that it counts. It doesn't matter that the athlete was capable of more—on the day that it mattered, he didn't produce.

The guidelines listed in Figure 3–1 should prove helpful in deciding on an appropriate training regimen that will get an athlete to a contest-ready state at the right time.

FIGURE 3-1. Training Tips for In-Season and Off-Season Conditioning Programs for All Sports

1. Identify the period of year in which your meets or contests are held. This is the in-season, when performance on a given day is most important. Your training prior to contest days should reflect ever-changing training states, weaknesses, strengths, and (in some cases) those of your opponents.

2. Keep accurate logs of your progress so that an objective assessment can be made of such weaknesses and strengths.

3. Typically, in-season training is more intense than off-season training (i.e., heavier weights, less frequent rest periods between sets, faster movements, etc.). Off-season training, on the other hand, should concentrate on eliminating observed weaknesses from the preceding in-season period. Off-season training should be more general in nature, while in-season training should more accurately reflect the nature of the skills in the athletes' respective sports.

4. Maintain constant vigilance during the in-season period for signs of overtraining. Back off in intensity if such signs begin to manifest themselves and increase the intensity in time enough to prepare for the upcoming meet or contest.

5. Fitness for one's sport should occupy the majority of training efforts in the off-season, and skill training should be done to the extent necessary to overcome deficiencies. Preseason and in-season training should maximize skill training, and conditioning should be engaged in to the extent that complete maintenance (or even improvement) of those fitness components necessary in one's sport is effected.

6. Athletes of all persuasions must, in the interest of maximizing the benefits of conditioning efforts, adhere to the basic principles of conditioning.

7. Weight training should be carried out by every athlete but should not be disruptive of often more important or productive forms of training. The two should complement each other.

8. One's choice of exercises should always reflect that person's sport requirements, from the standpoint of aerobic and anaerobic components involved as well as from the standpoint of which muscles are involved.

9. Always adhere to a nutritional regimen that will assist in maximizing progress in training and performance.

Also included in the list are those factors that are important in the off-season periods, when no contests or meets are scheduled for the near future. Each sport is different in regard to the length of in-season and off-season periods, but the requirements generally remain the same, regardless of the sport.

CIRCUIT TRAINING

In weight training parlance the term *circuit* refers to a series of exercises that are chosen for their relevance to one's sport. All good coaches and athletes know that it is important to analyze their sport to determine which muscles are most required in the conduct of their sport. Then, the exercises that most efficiently isolate the muscles identified as important are performed in a specified manner, depending on one's training objective. For example, strength would require fewer reps and endurance more reps (see Figure 2–4).

With the important exercises being identified, the circuit is performed in a sequential manner, with the most important muscles exercised first. In order to avoid overexerting any given muscle or muscle group, however, the trainee should refrain from putting two or more exercises together that emphasize the same muscle. Alternate them in such a way that both of these guidelines are met.

The most important aspect of circuit training is *time*. The trainee's "target time" for each circuit should be such that his or her heart rate is kept between the critical values of 60 percent and 85 percent of maximum. Figure 3–2 includes 60 percent and 85 percent heart rate values for different age groups. Allowing one's heart rate to fall below the critical value of 60 percent will result in very little (if any) cardiovascular benefit being derived, and working so fast that one's heart rate exceeds roughly 85 percent of his or her maximum heart rate will result in such a diminished capability for sufficient intensity that little strength improvement will be noticed. Further, fatigue will set in before any appreciable aerobic benefit is achieved if one's heart rate is allowed to go too high for any extended period of time.

To control the speed at which one's heart is beating, pausing

**FIGURE 3–2. Heart Rate Values during Exercise
for Different Age Groups (Continued)**

Age	Percentage of Maximum Heart Rate	Beats per Minute	Maximum Heart Rate	Beats per 10 Seconds
20	60	120	200	20
	85	170		28
25	60	117	195	19
	85	166		27
30	60	114	190	19
	85	162		27
35	60	111	185	18
	85	158		26
40	60	108	180	18
	85	153		25
45	60	105	175	17
	80	140		23
50	60	102	170	17
	75	128		21
60	60	96	160	16
70	60	90	150	15

Note: Exercising with a heart rate below 60 percent of one's maximum will result in little, if any, cardiovascular benefits as the stress is insufficient to force an adaptive response.

briefly to monitor heart rate is generally a good idea—do it between circuits. Placing your fingers on the right side of the throat, where the carotid artery is, is the best and quickest way to monitor your heart rate. Count the number of beats for 10 seconds. If the number of beats is between 20 and 28 for a 20-year-old athlete, for example, that athlete knows that his or her heart rate is between 120 and 170 beats per minute. Generally, the more important cardiovascular endurance is, the closer an athlete should attempt to get to the 85 percent figure. In any case, athletes inexperienced at weight training should restrict their efforts in circuit training to a heart rate closer to the 60 percent

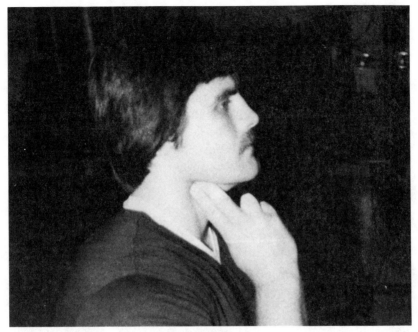

Measuring heart rate at the carotid artery.

value—it's safer and can be increased as experience is gained at the training exercises.

As age increases to a point where competitive sports at a championship level are not generally feasible, the need to push the heart rate to maximum levels becomes not only unimportant but risky. For that reason, Figure 3-2 includes somewhat lower upper limit values as age increases beyond 45.

To illustrate the circuit training method, let's use a hypothetical case of a wrestler wishing to improve not only muscular endurance but explosive power as well. (The reader is referred back to Figure 1-2. Wrestling requires, by most coaches' standards, about 50 percent aerobic fitness and 50 percent anaerobic.) The requirements of wrestling are such that all of the major muscles are important. Great strength must be there for breaking holds or explosively moving from one position to another and at the same time controlling the opponent. Since a wrestling match lasts for several minutes, and a wrestler may be required to wrestle several times in a tournament, muscular endurance is also of critical concern. The exercises of choice for the wrestler, then, will be as follows:

1. *Squats* for the legs and hips
2. *Bench presses* for the chest
3. *Crunchers* for the abdominals
4. *Pulldowns* for the latissimus
5. *Stiff-legged deadlifts* for the lower back
6. *Side bends* left and right for the obliques
7. *Curls* for the biceps
8. *Tricep extensions* for the triceps
9. *Bent rows* for the upper back
10. *Dumbbell presses* for the shoulders

These 10 exercises are the 10 stations in the circuit. The wrestler progresses from station to station, performing each exercise in the prescribed way, within a target time. Each successive trip through the circuit should be done within the target time. Typically, three or four trips through the circuit will be called for. (See Figure 3-3.)

In between trips the wrestler monitors his heart rate to ensure that his heart is working at the proper speed. If it is beating too slowly, his reps in each exercise are speeded up. If his heart is beating too fast, however, he must slow the pace accordingly. So the athlete's target time, generally speaking, will be determined according to how fast he must exercise to achieve the desired heart rate. At the beginning stages of training the wrestler would be well advised to target the 60 percent heart rate figure and progress as far as the 85 percent heart rate figure as the competitive season draws near.

Notice that the exercises in this athlete's circuit are arranged so that little overlap occurs with respect to the muscles being exercised. That is, the same muscle is not generally exercised twice in a row. This allows for better recovery of each muscle before it is exercised again.

Notice also that the exercises chosen are those that exercise all of the major muscle groups—one of the athlete's goals in wres-

FIGURE 3–3. A Circuit for Improving Strength and Endurance in Wrestling*

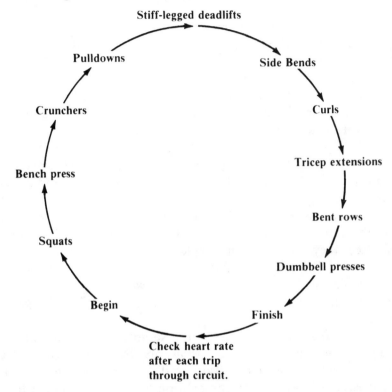

*Because the requirements of various sports differ from one another, the exercises in the circuit may be different for different sports. In fact, the exercises may vary within each sport, depending on the athlete's level of fitness, his or her position in the yearly cycle, and other factors.

tling that stems from that sport's requirements. Chapter 4 lists all of the exercises that are typically used in weight training for sports, and an illustration of each accompanies that listing. Chapter 5 is devoted to listing training programs for each of the major sports.

In this particular instance the athlete must improve his endurance as well as power. So, in concordance with the principles of conditioning (see Figure 2-4), his circuit training program will look something like this:

```
Percentage of maximum weight ................75-80
Duration of each set .................. 25-30 seconds
Reps per set ..................................15-20
Times through circuit ...........................3-4
Rest between sets ...................... 2-3 minutes
Speed per repetition ..................... maximum
Workouts per week ...............................7
```

In comparing this arrangement of training requirements with those presented in Figure 2-4, you will see that, while muscular endurance requirements are generally met, the lower end of the listed ranges is adhered to. Also, rather than having the movements required in each exercise done at a slow and sustained cadence, they are done with explosiveness so that power can be developed. The low end of the listed ranges is used so that the explosiveness factor can be adequately worked into the training scheme—fatigue could interfere with the athlete's ability to generate explosive movements.

As the off-season progresses, our example athlete will refine his training not only to coincide with his progress in achieving power or muscular endurance but also to reflect his position in the cycle. That is, as the season for competition draws nearer, target times will decrease, rest periods will decrease, weights will increase, speed of movements will increase, dietary regimen will be more closely scrutinized (wrestlers typically train at a body weight in excess of their competing weight, and as the competitive season draws near, some excess weight must be shed), and, in some cases, the number of workouts per week may increase or decrease. It will all depend on that athlete's (or his coach's) assessment of his progress.

During the entire off-season and preseason, any wrestling to be done is done before weight training or other forms of conditioning (except stretching for flexibility). This guarantees that the wrestler can work his skills while fresh so as to avoid injury and maximize the motor learning process.

This sample circuit for a wrestler was presented as a guide for other athletes interested in developing their own circuits. The kinds of considerations that went into devising the example circuit will be similar to those of any athlete. Circuit training is probably the most widely used system of weight training among endurance athletes. Sometimes it is the best system, though others may prove better in certain sports or circumstances. But this system certainly stands out as the easiest to institute for most athletes. This is because of the physical layout of most weight-training facilities, with little space between pieces of equipment; the larger number of athletes that are typically present in the weight room at the same time; and its simplicity of design.

If large groups of athletes are circuit training at the same time, coaches will typically blow a whistle at the end of a target time for each exercise, indicating that all athletes rotate to the next exercise. When training on your own, however, it is advisable to seek a gym or time that is more conducive to training without interruption or at your own target pace.

INTERVAL TRAINING

Most exercise physiologists agree that interval training is the "Cadillac" of all endurance training methods. Interval training typically consists of short bursts of submaximal work alternating with short active rest (walking around) periods. During the work phase the heart rate should be kept between 60 percent and 85 percent of the athlete's maximum heart rate (see Figure 3–2). For most competing athletes, however, a heart rate of 150 or more is recommended, because the intensity of the work will determine the amount of benefit derived. However, work should in no case progress for more than approximately one minute in intervals requiring the use of weights. Research has shown that working at a rate of 80 percent of one's maximum heart rate for between 30 and 60 seconds allows the oxygen transport system to be fully stressed and at the same time decreases the fatigue level (lactic acid buildup in the working muscles). This reduced fatigue is designed to allow the athlete to increase the volume of work.

The exact amount of time for each interval of work depends on the sport one is training for and on the individual athlete's fitness requirements. The more aerobic the sport, the longer the work interval; the more anaerobic the sport, the shorter the work interval. Putting it another way, if an athlete's goal is to maximize a muscle's strength or power capabilities, the work interval should be close to the 30-second mark. If, however, his requirements are for endurance in the muscle being worked, the work interval should be about one minute in duration. The amount of weight will vary directly with the duration of the work interval as well. Heavier weights are required for shorter work intervals, and lighter weights are required for the longer work intervals.

The rest intervals should be of sufficient duration to allow the heart rate to return to a level that is below the 60 percent maximum heart rate figure for the training athlete. This rest interval is necessary in order to prepare the athlete for another interval of work. As described in the preceding section on circuit training, one's heart rate should be monitored between intervals. Placing the fingers on the right side of the throat, over the carotid artery, is the easiest way to measure heart rate. Photo 3–1 on page 41 illustrates how to measure the heart rate. Another easy method is to measure the time it takes for the heart to beat 15 times. Immediately after the work interval the heart should beat 15 times in fewer than 5.6 seconds. The next work interval should begin when the time for 15 beats goes up to 7.5 seconds.

Perhaps the complexities of interval training with weights can best be illustrated with an example. Let's say that a basketball player wants to improve his endurance for getting up and down the court. Also, since he must be able to rebound time after time, as well as be able to move explosively in any direction while guarding an opponent or eluding him while dribbling the ball, he must also possess exceptional power in his legs. Fair upper body strength is also required for skirmishes under the board.

Since the muscles of the legs (the quadriceps, hamstrings, and calves) are the most important ones for basketball players, they should be exercised first. The athlete begins his work interval with squats. At the top of each squat a toe raise is performed to exercise the calves. Each repetition is done with maximum explosiveness, and the weight should approach the 75–80 percent of maximum range of effort. Squatting in this manner for at least 30 seconds should be done. The athlete's heart rate is then measured. If it has not risen to at least 150 beats per minute, either the speed of the repetitions needs to be increased in subsequent work intervals or the number of reps (e.g., the duration of the work interval) needs to be increased. The athlete then walks around (active rest) until his heart rate is again at a manageable level (about 120 beats per minute). When the athlete counts 15 beats of the heart in about 7.5 seconds the next set of squats can be performed. Again, they are done so that the heart is working at about 80 percent of its maximum—near 150–160 beats per minute.

This pattern of alternating work and rest intervals should be repeated three or four times for each exercise. No fewer than six exercises (up to a maximum of ten) should comprise a single workout. Figure 3–4 illustrates how the entire workout should progress for our example basketball player. Other athletes should gear the intensity of their work intervals and rest intervals to their individual requirements. Again, longer, less intense work intervals are generally recommended for the more aerobic sports, and shorter, more intense work intervals are more suited to the more anaerobic sports. The rest intervals will always be such that the heart rate is allowed to return to a manageable level (approximately 120 beats per minute, or 15 beats in about 7.5 seconds) before beginning the next work interval. As one's endurance improves, the rest intervals will become shorter and shorter.

A note of caution is necessary at this point. It is very easy to overtrain when using the interval training method. Athletes must be aware that peaking too soon before a contest or game is often devastating to performance. To avoid becoming contest-ready too early prior to the beginning of the competitive season, each athlete must control the intensity of his or her training. Using intervals of 30–60 seconds will often bring an athlete to contest or game readiness in about four to six weeks. So, during the off-season the intensity of each work interval should be such that the weights used are well below the 80–85 percent of maximum level. As the contest or game draws nearer (to about four to six weeks) the amount of weight being used can be increased to the recommended levels—not before.

There are many ways of manipulating the amount of overload

FIGURE 3–4. A Typical Interval Training Program for a Basketball Player* (Continued)

Exercise	Approximate Heart Rate	Approximate Number of Reps	Approximate Time (minutes)
1. Warm-up and stretching	—	—	4–5
2. Squats and toe raises	150	20	1
3. Rest	120	—	1–3
4. Repeat 2 & 3 about 3 more times			
5. Bench press	150	20	1
6. Rest	120	—	1–3
7. Repeat 5 & 6 about 3 more times			
8. Crunchers	150	20	1
9. Rest	120	—	1–3
10. Repeat 8 & 9 about 3 more times			
11. Dumbbell presses	150	20	1
12. Rest	120	—	1–3
13. Repeat 11 & 12 about 3 more times			
14. Curls	150	20	1
15. Rest	120	—	1–3
16. Repeat 14 & 15 about 3 more times			
17. Hamstring curls	150	20	1
18. Rest	120	—	1–3
19. Repeat 17 & 18 about 3 more times—workout finished			

* Because the requirements of individuals or sports generally vary, the exercises described here may vary as well. Each athlete in every sport should take his or her sport requirements into consideration when constructing a conditioning program.

**FIGURE 3-5. Methods of Overload
Employed in Interval Training**

Method of Overload	Expected Outcome(s)
Increase duration of work interval (to about one minute)	CV endurance
Decrease the duration of the work interval (to about 30 seconds)	Muscular endurance and strength
Increase the intensity of the work interval	Muscular endurance and strength
Increase the intensity of the activity during the rest interval	CV & muscular endurance
Increase the length of the workout	CV & muscular endurance

being employed in interval training. The five most common methods are listed in Figure 3-5, along with the expected outcome(s) of each.

As was the case in the circuit training method described earlier in this chapter, the exact exercises one chooses will always depend on the nature of one's sport requirements and individual goals. All of the exercises that are typically done with weights are described in Chapter 4, and sample programs for many of the most popular sports can be found in Chapter 5.

PARCOURSE TRAINING

Parcourse training is a recent concept in the area of endurance training, having appeared less than 10 years ago. Like most systems of training, it evolved from many different systems and ideas, but parcourse training was probably affected most by a system of training used by European long-distance runners more than 50 years ago, called *fartlek training*. In order to best describe the general tenets of parcourse training, a look at the origin of fartlek training will be helpful.

Gosta Homer, the Swedish track and field coach during the 1948 Olympiad, had this to say to an American colleague:

My opinion is . . . that it is not the races run that make the runner, but rather his training methods. Here in Sweden we saw ourselves conquered by the Finns; we gained a certain standard until I, in the middle of 1930, decided to try to create something new, something that suited our mind and the nature of our country. I rejected the American opinion that the runners should have fixed distances to run during their daily training schedule; I realized of course the great importance of that, but I wanted to give the boys a feeling of self-creating; I wanted to get them to understand themselves, and then fix the training according to their own individuality. Speed and endurance are the marks a runner should follow in his training. Following these lines I made up a system, that I call *fartlek* (meaning in English, play-of-speed, or speed play), and it runs as follows:

The athlete should train from one to two hours each day, according to the following schedule:

1. Easy running from five to ten minutes (as a warm-up)
2. Steady, hard speed for one to two kilometers
3. Rapid walking for about five minutes
4. Easy running, broken by wind-sprints of from 50 meters to 60 meters, and repeated until you feel a little tired
5. Easy running with three or four swift steps now and then (in reality these swift steps would be like the sudden speeding up of a runner during the race when he tries to fight off a challenger who is trying to pass him. The body suddenly lurches forward, and three or four sudden, quick steps are taken).
6. Full speed uphill 150 meters to 200 meters
7. Fast pace for one minute following this trial of strength described in (6). The above described work can be repeated until the end of the period of the workout; but every athlete should well remember that he must not feel tired but rather stimulated after the training.

This early form of fartlek training evolved into a system of training that made use of the local terrain and obstacles on the running course: over hills, down through wooded gullies, over logs and fences, speeding up and slowing down in a fashion similar to Homer's fartlek. The exact course and system of overcoming obstacles should coincide with the goals of the runner or athlete. In other words, fartlek training evolved into a highly sophisticated and systematized form of training that afforded the athlete opportunities throughout the course of a workout to overcome noted weaknesses in his or her performance.

This is exactly what parcourse training is all about. The original parcourses were, in actuality, built on terrain that afforded the athlete hills, trees to dodge, logs to jump over, and important stations along the way that included exercises for various muscle groups. Chin-ups, sit-ups, stretching, dumbbell presses, rope skipping, and a host of other exercises the athlete deemed appropriate were included in the parcourse. The athlete was required to run (sprint, jog, or walk) from station to station, often over terrain that was, in itself, a test of strength or endurance.

Needless to say, parcourse training is suitable, in the fashion described above, to pursuing practically any objective that an endurance athlete may set. Parcourse training has been adapted to athletes' needs using exclusively weight training exercises at each station, though the running portion should remain intact. As with circuit training and interval training programs (described earlier), an example of a parcourse system should be enlightening.

For our example of parcourse training, let's use a cross-country skier. The cross-country skier requires great cardiovascular endurance. But excellent strength (for overcoming obstacles along the way) and muscular endurance are also essential, owing to the repetitive nature of the sport. Pulling and pushing with the arms, climbing hills, negotiating jumps and moguls on the course, and enduring the cold temperatures normally encountered all add up to one criterion: the athlete must possess all-around fitness. Endurance alone or strength alone simply isn't enough for such a demanding sport. The system of training that's best suited for such an athlete is, without question, parcourse training. In the off-season, when there is no snow available, or when the proper terrain is not to be found nearby, a large gymnasium or field will do. The weight-training equipment needn't be spread out—simply running to the other end of the gym or field and back to the weight area will suffice.

Figure 3-6 illustrates how a parcourse system can be mapped out in a large gym or field. As with circuit training and interval training, heart rate is very important. In the case of parcourse training, however, the athlete attempts to train at a steady state. That is, the heart rate is controlled so that enough oxygen is supplied to the heart and working muscles to allow the athlete to continue working throughout the workout. Extreme fatigue is to be avoided in the interest of maintaining as high an intensity as possible throughout the workout period. Typically, beginners in

FIGURE 3-6. Sample Parcourse in a Large Gymnasium or Athletic Field for Cross-Country Skiers*

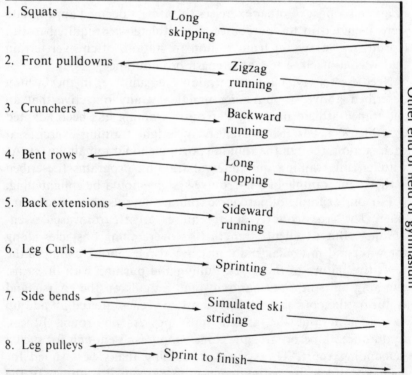

1. Squats — Long skipping
2. Front pulldowns — Zigzag running
3. Crunchers — Backward running
4. Bent rows — Long hopping
5. Back extensions — Sideward running
6. Leg Curls — Sprinting
7. Side bends — Simulated ski striding
8. Leg pulleys — Sprint to finish

Other end of field or gymnasium

*The weight-training equipment is located at one end of the field or gym. The various methods of traversing the field or gym and to the weight-training equipment are designed to provide the skier with all forms of movement suited to simulating the varied terrain and movements encountered in cross-country skiing. The parcourse should be repeated at least three times in succession, maintaining a training heart rate of approximately 150 beats per minute.

such a training program will be able to tolerate heart rates of about 140–150 beats per minute, while highly trained athletes may be able to push it up to a sustained 160–165 beats per minute. Trained athletes will also find that they will be able to sustain greater levels of intensity throughout the workout, thereby making their efforts even more productive.

The most common way to lay out a parcourse is to consider it a special form of circuit training, replete with exercises, target times for each circuit, and monitoring of the heart rate between trips through the circuit. Rather than being called a *circuit,* however, the group of exercises is called a *parcourse* because of the running required between stations.

The exercises listed in the example parcourse in Figure 3–6 are illustrated and described in Chapter 4. In Chapter 5 various systems of training are illustrated for many popular sports.

As with the circuit training and interval training systems described earlier, reference to Figure 3–2 will assist in monitoring heart rate and maintaining the appropriate level of intensity throughout the parcourse. If the heart rate is too fast, reducing running speed or exercise rate may be required. However, if the heart is beating slower than about 140 beats per minute, it will be advisable to speed up either the running between stations or the performance of the exercise.

PERIPHERAL HEART ACTION TRAINING

Peripheral heart action training (called PHA training) had its inception among the ranks of bodybuilders around the early 1960s in the United States. It was designed to assist in lowering the physique artist's body fat percentage, thereby making the underlying musculature more visible. The theory was that altering one's basal metabolic rate would burn more calories and enhance the efficiency with which ingested food was utilized. It worked well.

The program that these early bodybuilders used, however, also had to be designed to maximize muscle size. Thus, considerably heavier weights and lower repetitions were typically used. The bodybuilder concentrated on maintaining as high a heart rate throughout the PHA workout as possible while at the same time allowing him to lift the heavy weights for the required number of repetitions and sets.

The PHA system of training has only recently been studied and tested for usefulness in promoting cardiovascular and local muscular endurance. To adapt it to these ends, the number of repetitions was increased, and the rapidity with which the system was traversed was increased. Again it worked—and remarkably well.

The PHA system got its name from the fact that each exercise was intended for a muscle or muscle group far removed from the preceding one (i.e., located *peripherally* from the preceding one). This arrangement of exercises is designed to do a number of things. First, the heart is required to work constantly, shunting blood to the area being exercised, then again to the next area of the body, and the next, and so forth, until the entire sequence of exercises is completed at least three times.

Since no muscle is required to work too long, there is little possibility that too much stress will be placed on that muscle. It has ample time to recover before it is blitzed again. This is good because, while the heart is working hard throughout the entire sequence, each muscle has a chance to recover enough to permit maximum overload again—fatigue of the individual muscle(s) is not a factor limiting effort. Only one's cardiovascular efficiency will limit one's effort.

In other words, the emphasis in PHA training is on cardiovascular efficiency. The weights being lifted, of course, will increase strength and tone to a degree that is commensurate with the amount of intensity being applied. Because no muscle is taxed for great lengths of time, however, it is not the best system of training for local muscular endurance training. Circuit training and (especially) interval training are the best for the individual muscle's endurance.

A peripheral heart action system is typically comprised of four sequences of exercises, with each sequence being comprised of three or four exercises. Since each sport's fitness requirements vary, the exercises one chooses will differ accordingly. Figure 3–7 is an illustration of a PHA system that may be suitable for a soccer player. In soccer good overall body strength is required, as is exceptional cardiovascular endurance. However, the local muscular endurance requirements in the game of soccer are minimal,

FIGURE 3-7. A Peripheral Heart Action System of Weight Training for a Soccer Player*

Sequence 1	Sequence 2	Sequence 3	Sequence 4
Squats	Leg curls	Leg pulleys	Toe Raises
Dumbbell presses	Lat pulldowns	Side bends	Lateral raises
Crunchers	High pulls	Curls	Tricep extensions

1. Do about 20 reps of squats with a weight that is equivalent to about 70 percent of your maximum.
2. Without resting, go on to dumbbell presses in like fashion and then on to crunchers, maintaining a heart rate of about 150 beats per minute throughout.
3. Repeat the exercises in Sequence 1 three or four times, resting at the completion of these sets until your heart rate is back to about 120 beats per minute. Then go on to Sequence 2, rest, proceed to Sequence 3, rest, and finish up with Sequence 4.
4. For increased power or strength, use more weight and fewer reps and do all movements with controlled explosiveness.
5. For increased cardiovascular endurance, use lighter weights for higher reps and minimize rest intervals while maximizing speed through each sequence, thereby maintaining as high a heart rate as tolerable without undue fatigue limiting training intensity.

* Each sport and each individual has different requirements. Therefore, each athlete must carefully select those exercises and training methods that will maximize goal attainment.

making the PHA system of weight training the method of choice.

The athlete begins with Sequence 1, performing about 20 repetitions of each exercise in the sequence without resting between sets. These exercises are repeated for three or four sets nonstop. Then a short rest is taken to allow the heart to return to a manageable level (about 120 beats per minute). The second sequence is repeated similarly and is followed by a rest period. Then the third and fourth sequences are completed in like fashion. The heart rate should be maintained at about 150–160 beats per minute during the conduct of each sequence of exercises (see Figure 3–2 for exact prescribed heart rate limits).

As with circuit training, interval training, and parcourse training, one's heart rate is monitored between sets by placing the fingers on the right side of the throat, where the carotid artery is. Counting the number of beats in 10 seconds (refer to Figure 3-2) or the time it takes for the heart to beat 15 times (6.7 seconds for exercise and 7.5 seconds for rest period) are the methods most practically applied when monitoring one's heart rate.

The exercises listed in Figure 3-7 can be found in Chapter 4— complete descriptions and illustrations of all the most commonly used weight training exercises are listed there. Also, detailed exercise regimens for many different sports are presented in Chapter 5.

SUMMARY

The basic principles of conditioning have been formulated over the years on the basis of hard scientific research. They are not the products of simple trial and error or of some whimsical coach's fantasies. The systems of weight training that are described in this chapter are, however, trial-and-error attempts to maximize the proficiency with which the basic principles of conditioning are implemented. Experience has shown that these four are excellent means of improving cardiovascular endurance, muscular strength, and local muscular endurance to varying degrees. Each has its peculiarities and uses. It is up to the astute coach or athlete to determine which is best suited for maximizing training efficiency.

Circuit training, interval training, parcourse training, and peripheral heart action training have all evolved over the years and have been adapted to accommodate the particularly versatile progressive resistance system of training with weights. The examples that accompany each system are designed for use with a particular sport but may have varying degrees of applicability to other athletes. Using the examples as guides rather than gospel will help in finding the most appropriate system for each individual.

Chapter 4 lists and describes each of the major exercises performed with weights, while Chapter 5 details sample weight training programs for many popular sports.

4

The Major Exercises for Sports and Fitness

INTRODUCTION

This chapter illustrates the beginning and ending positions of each of the most commonly used weight-training exercises for (1) the arms, (2) the chest, (3) the shoulders, (4) the upper and lower back, (5) the midsection, and (6) the legs. These are the body parts most frequently identified in classifying weight-training exercises.

In many cases an exercise will be illustrated with barbells. However, dumbbells can very often be used in lieu of barbells, particularly by athletes wishing to include some of the smaller stabilizer and assisting muscles in a particular movement. Since the dumbbell is held in one hand, there is a balancing or stabilizing factor that must be contended with, and exercising the muscles that assist in this regard can often prove helpful both in increasing overall strength and in injury prevention.

Next to dumbbells, barbells are by far the most desirable form of weight training. Machines that force the user to move the weight up and down a slide arrangement are also fine but lack the benefit of getting at the synergistic and stabilizer muscles in the same way that dumbbells can. Since most modern spas have both free weights (i.e., dumbbells and barbells) and machines, all of these forms of weight-training equipment are used in the illustrations. However, to reiterate, for the competing athlete, dumbbells are generally the best. If the nature of the exercise precludes their use, or if they are not available in the desired sizes, barbells should be used. And if barbells are not available or practical due to the nature of the exercise, use the machines. Cam machines (such as Nautilus equipment), pulley machines, friction machines, hydraulic machines, and a host of other futuristic contraptions are commonly found in most spas. All have their uses, and the wise athlete will seek out professional assistance in the proper use of these machines.

Each exercise is designed to do one thing—isolate a given muscle or muscle group. This is in concordance with the basic principle of conditioning noted in Chapter 2. Exactly how each exercise is performed with regard to the speed, amount of weight, number of repetitions or sets, and exact movement pattern is always to be governed by the athlete's specific sport requirements and training goals. Before embarking on a weight-training program for any purpose, one's goals must be clearly identified so that the precisely correct methods of weight training can be employed. Science has shown us how to accomplish each of our respective fitness goals, and deviating from these scientific methods will only result in prolonging the time before goal attainment or (at the worst) failure. Figure 2–4 provides a good summary of how each of the typical goals of size, strength or power, muscular endurance, and cardiovascular endurance can be achieved through scientific weight training. Employing the appropriate exercises for your particular sport or goals is the next step. And the final step is perseverance. Stick to your program as it will invariably pay rich dividends.

EXERCISES FOR THE ARMS

Almost all sports require the use of the arms. In most endurance sports local muscular endurance is needed most. For example, in wrestling, crew, swimming, gymnastics, and cross-country skiing sustained or repetitive arm movements require that conditioning efforts for arm muscles concentrate on local muscular endurance. However, a good deal of strength is also often needed so most training efforts will reflect this requirement by including sets with slightly heavier weights done for fewer repetitions.

The most basic movements of the arm are elbow flexion and

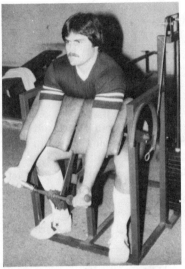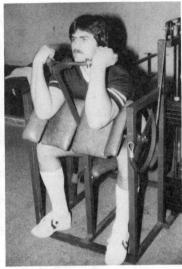

Bicep Curl: Curls can be done with a dumbbell in each hand, a barbell, an "E-Z Curl" bar, or a machine. All serve the same function—improving the size, shape, strength, or endurance of the bicep muscles of the upper arm. Be sure to exercise the biceps through their full range of motion for best results.

Tricep Extension: This exercise will affect the back of the upper arms and can be done with pulley systems (as shown), dumbbells, a barbell, or an "E-Z Curl" bar.

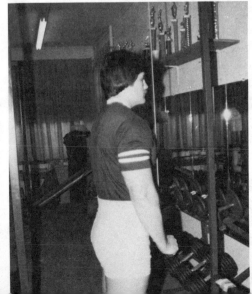

Thor's Hammer: Aptly named for the fabled Norse god of thunder who wielded a mighty hammer, this exercise will develop the forearms' muscles that control pronation and supination—two muscle groups that are generally overlooked in conditioning programs, despite their importance in many sports activities.

Wrist Curl: This forearm exercise will develop the extensors and flexors of the wrist. Like Thor's hammer exercises, wrist curls are an indispensable exercise for many classes of athletes, particularly for sports involving swinging an implement.

extension and forearm pronation and supination. Thus, there are four basic exercises for the arms: (1) curls (biceps), (2) tricep extensions (triceps), (3) Thor's hammer inward (pronation), and (4) Thor's hammer outward (supination). Many fitness experts include wrist exercises in the arm sections of training manuals. Wrist curls forward and backward are typically done to strengthen the wrists for sports such as golf, baseball, and racquet sports.

EXERCISES FOR THE SHOULDERS

Since the arms are attached to the shoulders, the shoulders are important because they must stabilize so the arms can perform

Lateral Raise: This exercise develops the mid-shoulder muscles (medial deltoids). The range of movement need not extend to arms' length above the head, as the deltoids act only until the arms are about parallel with the ground—straight out from the sides. It can be performed in a number of ways, including the dumbbell and machine methods depicted here.

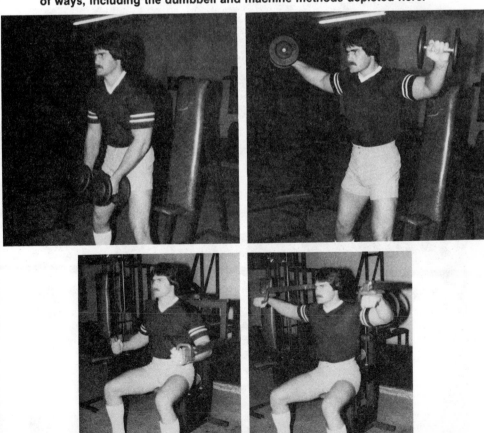

Frontal Raise: Designed to affect the frontal portion of the shoulders (anterior deltoids), this exercise is properly done when the dumbbells are raised to about eye level and the arms are out front as shown.

Inverted Flyes: This exercise can be done with dumbbells or with cable systems (as shown). It develops the muscles of the upper back and, most particularly, the rear portion of the shoulders (posterior deltoids).

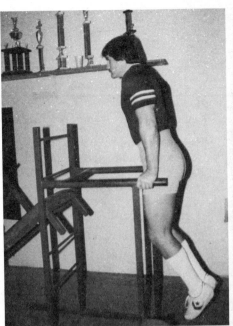
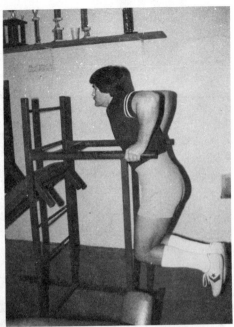

Dip: This exercise has become very popular among weight-training enthusiasts because it is a compound exercise, having an effect on more than one muscle. It develops the anterior deltoids, triceps, and chest and is equally efficient in all three body areas. To maximize shoulder development, attempt to maintain an erect body position and dip as deeply as possible.

Military Press: When doing pressing movements, it is advisable to wear a supportive belt, if standing, to assist in preventing injury to the lower back. However, if done as shown (seated), this problem does not arise, and the exercise can be done quite safely. It is an excellent shoulder developer and offers some benefit to the triceps (arms) as well.

Upright Row: This exercise is generally done with a barbell and is designed to develop the shoulders, particularly the middle portion (medial deltoids). The bar should be kept close to the body during the upward pull.

their respective functions more efficiently. But movements of the shoulder joint are also very important during the conduct of most sports. There are many exercises for the shoulder—it is a complex joint capable of movement in all planes. The basic movements are pulling, pushing, throwing, raising, and lowering of the arms, and circumduction (rotation). The exercises illustrated here represent the most important and common movements found in most sports.

EXERCISES FOR THE CHEST

The muscles of the chest are actually used to move the shoulder joint, and exercises for them are often classified under those for the shoulders. Because most people think of the chest as a part of

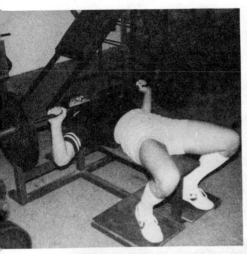

Bench Press: This exercise can be performed with a barbell, dumbbell, or machines. All are relatively similar, with dumbbells being the preferred exercise method for athletes. It is the best way to build the muscles of the chest.

Incline Bench Press: This has become a popular exercise for developing the upper portion of the chest. Generally, the best incline for this exercise will be between 20 and 30 degrees. Elevating the incline above 30 degrees will take the emphasis away from the chest and put it more on the shoulders.

Pullover: This exercise, if done over a period of many months, has been known to assist in enlarging the rib cage by acting on the small intercostal muscles (small muscles between the ribs). It will also assist in developing the latissimus muscles, located under the arms and sweeping across the back. A larger rib cage will, theoretically, allow for a greater vital capacity (i.e., the amount of air one can draw into the lungs), owing to the greater room for expansion within the rib cage.

Pec Deck: This machine exercise is a comfortable way of performing a chest exercise and is quite efficient. Typically, however, great loads cannot be handled because most machines are not equipped with enough weight or are not designed so that maximum stress can be isolated in the chest muscles. But for high-rep work such as what may be required of an endurance-oriented athlete, it can be as efficient as bench presses.

the body distinct from the shoulders, however, the exercises for the chest are listed separately. There are only two primary muscles in the chest, the clavicular pectoralis (upper chest), and the sternal pectoralis (lower chest). Thus, there are only two basic exercises for the chest, though many offshoots of these basic exercises are done around most gyms. A few of the more common ones are illustrated here.

EXERCISES FOR THE BACK

Many exercises for the upper back are related to the shoulder girdle and shoulder joint but are typically listed separately for

Bent Row: From a bent-over position, the weight is pulled up to the chest while trying, as much as possible, to relax the arms and allow the muscles of the upper back to do the work. The rhomboid muscles act in rotating the scapulae downward and drawing them inward toward the spine.

Frontal Pulldown: With arms held straight, the cable handle is drawn downward toward the waist. This exercise also affects the latissimus muscles, though from a different angle.

 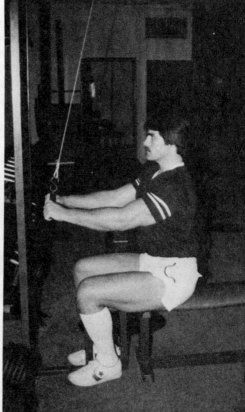

Long Cable Pull: This exercise affects the latissimus dorsi muscles (those long, sweeping muscles that give one the V look). Try to key on those muscles mentally and relax the arms as much as possible.

Shrug: The muscles near the neck, called the *trapezius* muscles, are important as shoulder girdle elevators and stabilizers in many sports. Simply shrug your shoulders with the weight held in the hands.

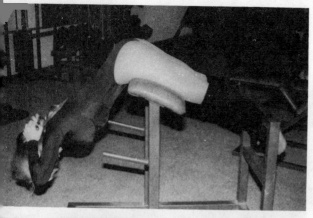

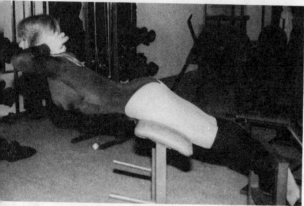

Hyperextension: Designed to be a lower back exercise, this is an indispensable tool for those athletes who must do heavy pulling or lifting movements, as it will greatly assist in preventing the all-too-prevalent incidence of lower back injury in sports. Actually, it is a misnamed exercise, as only extension to a straight body position is indicated—it is not advisable or necessary to hyperextend the spine to a position beyond that recommended (as depicted).

Stiff-Legged Deadlift: Like the hyperextension, this exercise is designed to develop the lower back. However, it has the added advantage of developing the gluteals (the rump muscles) and the hamstrings (back of the upper leg). Start slow and use a light weight to begin this exercise, as it is potentially a dangerous exercise. Don't overtax yourself at first.

Pulldown: Like long cable pulls and frontal pulldowns, this exercise is for the latissimus dorsi muscles. Because it acts directly on the lats from a very efficient angle, it is probably the best exercise for that purpose.

High Pull: This exercise is to be done explosively. It will assist in developing explosiveness as well as offering the benefit of teaching one to use many muscles of the body in a sequential pattern so that total explosiveness is maximized. The lower range of movement is done with the legs; then, as the bar ascends, the back becomes involved, then the shoulders and arms—all in sequence such that the sum force is equal to that generated by all three muscle groups involved. It is an indispensable exercise for most athletes.

clarity. Bear in mind that since the muscles of the shoulder girdle and shoulder joint bear heavily on most arm movements (i.e., they act as stabilizers and assistant movers for most arm movements), they should be included in any program for sports where arm movements are essential.

EXERCISES FOR THE MIDSECTION

In reference to the midsection perhaps more than to any other body part, people ask, "How do I get rid of this?" They mean, of course, the flab around the waist. Fat and muscle are two separate types of tissue, and one has little bearing on the other. The fat is removed through proper diet, while the muscles underlying the midsection are developed in strength, tone, and endurance through proper training.

The role of the midsection in most sports is that of a stabilizer. When one is throwing, kicking, running, or pushing, the abdominal muscles contract statically in order to prevent unwanted movement from the nonmoving half of the body. Strength, therefore, is the most typical training goal for the abdominals. In some sports, however, the abdominals are required to possess great endurance. Swimmers, for example, must keep their abdominals contracted for prolonged periods of time in order to prevent their midsection from sagging down into the water, thereby causing a drag. Also, gymnasts must statically hold leg or upper body positions for long periods of time, taxing the endurance capabilities of the abdominals. The following exercises are recommended for the midsection.

A lot of myths regarding proper exercises for the midsection have persisted over the years. The most damaging one of all is that sit-ups are the best exercise. They are not. They are probably the worst exercise you can do, because of the tremendous stress imposed on the lower back. The psoas muscle travels from the lumbar region of the spine to the femur bones of the upper legs. It is a hip flexor muscle, not a midsection muscle. When performing a sit-up, the abdominals remain in static contraction while the psoas muscle does the work of raising the trunk (or legs if leg raises are being done). Little benefit is derived for the untaxed

Cruncher: This exercise replaces the age-old (and now advised against) sit-ups. It effectively isolates the abdominals and thereby protects the lower back from the trauma that regular sit-ups cause. When performed correctly, the ribs are drawn toward the pelvis from a position where the abdominal muscles are stretched. There is no hip action involved—no bending at the waist. Only trunk flexion is effected by the abdominals, and that is all this exercise calls for. It can also be done in reverse fashion, so that the pelvis is drawn toward the ribs instead of vice versa.

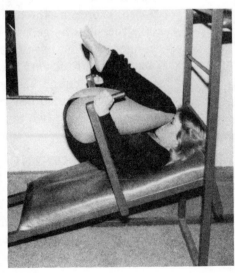

Side Bend: The oblique muscles located on your sides (to the right and left of your abdominals) are typically overlooked. Yet they are nearly as important as the abdominals in achieving a truly strong midsection so often required in sports. Do not neglect them.

abdominals, and a lot of harm is done to the lumbar spine. Stay away from sit-ups and leg raises!

Also, exercising the obliques (the muscles of the sides) does not make the sides bulge, as many people think. The obliques become stronger, making twisting movements (as in throwing or swinging a bat) more proficient. The increased tone of the obliques actually assists in flattening them and preventing them from bulging. The bulge observed on most people is comprised of fat anyway, not muscle. These are two unrelated problems.

EXERCISES FOR THE LEGS

Practically all sports require strong legs. Most sport skills are done while standing on the legs! And, if it isn't strength that's needed, it is muscular endurance. A lot of sports that are tradi-tionally thought of as requiring minimal use of the legs have been

Lunge: This is an excellent exercise for isolating the quadriceps (located in the front of the upper leg). Simply lunge forward to the position depicted and push back to an upright position again. Repeat the movement with both legs.

Squat: This is very possibly the king of all exercises, since it assists in developing so many muscle groups. Its primary intent, however, is to develop strong or enduring legs—and buttocks. With the weight on your shoulders as depicted, descend to a position where the tops of your thighs are about parallel to the ground. Then stand back up, keeping your torso straight up and down and the weight centered over the middle of your feet (not on your toes or heels). This exercise will *not* adversely affect your knees as so many people believe—it can if done incorrectly, however, so use caution and have a spotter on each side of the bar to assist if the weight proves too heavy or if fatigue prevents you from rising.

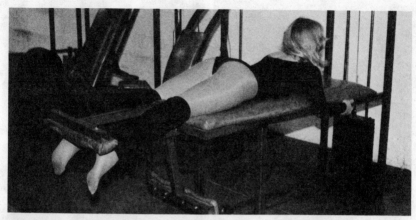

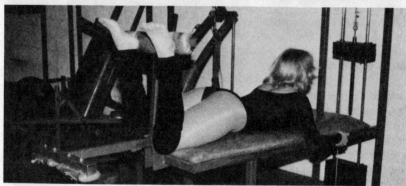

Leg Curl: Since most sports require strong quadriceps, an imbalance often occurs between the muscles of the front and back of the upper legs. This can place undue strain on the knees. So leg curls are a vital exercise for most athletes and will go a long way in helping to prevent knee injuries. As a general rule of thumb, you should be able to curl (with the hamstrings) about one-third to one-half as much as you can extend with (using your quadriceps).

found, through cinematographic analyses (slow-motion films) and biomechanical analyses (arithmetic models) actually to rely heavily on the legs for the initial impetus. Swinging a baseball bat, a tennis racquet, a golf club, shot putting, throwing, and dozens of other common sport skills require great leg strength or endurance. They are the most important muscles for many sports.

People walk and run throughout their lifetime. The legs develop to the point of being able to handle this everyday stress.

Leg Extension: This is the other half of the leg curl movement. It develops the quadriceps, located in the front of the upper leg. The quadriceps typically are much stronger than the hamstrings and thereby cause a strain on the knee joint. By maintaining an equitable ratio of strength between the quadriceps and hamstrings (roughly one to two or three), many knee injuries may be avoided.

Hack Squat: This exercise is exactly like squats, with one quite important exception: it eliminates back involvement. So it is to be used by athletes suffering from sore backs or individuals who can't do squats because of lower back pain. There is no reason why the legs must suffer because of an injury or other problem with the back.

Toe Raise: This is an indispensable exercise for runners and
jumpers. The gastrocnemius
muscles are the calf muscles located in the back of the lower leg
and are used in pushing with the
toes, as in running or jumping.

In-Out Thigh Exercise: This is fast becoming a popular exercise, particularly with men and women who have been inactive for too long. The
muscles of the inner thigh (the adductors) as well as the gluteus minimus
(the muscle behind your hip pocket) are the two muscles affected. Great
for toning these areas, but not the greatest exercise for athletes—squats
will do the trick for them.

Leg Kick Inward and Outward: This exercise is designed to condition the adductors and abductors of the upper legs. The muscles located on the inside and outside portions of the legs are actually exercised when doing squats to a fair degree, so this is an auxiliary exercise for that purpose. But it is also useful for those who, because of knee or back injury, are unable to perform squats.

The stresses of sport, particularly at the championship level, are considerable and require something more than simply running or walking more than usual. The legs require weight training. Weight training is the very best and most efficient system of applying stress to the legs—cycling, sprinting, swimming, or other forms of leg exercise are of insufficient intensity to force an adaptive process in the muscles of the legs. Here are the most common leg exercises:

SOME COMMON SIMULATION EXERCISES FOR SPORTS

One of the basic principles of conditioning requires that, as the competitive season draws near, time be spent on honing the skills of your sport to a fine edge. This, of course, means repetitive

Sport Movement Simulation Exercise: In this particular example of a sport movement being simulated with weights, the athlete is going through the movement of a shot putter. Similar exercises can be devised for batters, golfers, tennis players, and a host of other sport movements.

drills—practice. But it also means some rather specialized weight-training exercises that are designed to facilitate skill acquisition while, at the same time, greater strength or endurance is achieved through the skilled movement.

These exercises are performed by simulating sport skills against greater-than-normal resistance. Care must be taken to avoid improper movements; practicing the wrong "groove" will be more harmful than beneficial. Stay as close to the skill's actual movement pattern and speed as possible, using a weight, implement, or pulley system that offers slightly greater resistance than normal.

Examples of the types of movements that can be performed against supranormal resistance are: (1) throwing, (2) shot putting, (3) swimming strokes, (4) blocking (football), (5) crew (rowing), and (6) swinging a club, bat, or racquet.

Most typically, the result of such simulation training is greater strength through the movement. This, in turn, results in greater absolute endurance—greater strength endurance. That is, the throw or swing or other skill can be performed with great strength time after time—not just the first few times—before fatigue limits effort.

5

Weight-Training Programs for Selected Sports

Chapter 3 listed the four basic weight-training programs that are best suited for endurance-type sports. They are: (1) circuit training, (2) interval training, (3) parcourse training, and (4) peripheral heart action training.

The training programs listed in this chapter follow the basic tenets of these major training systems, with a few small but significant exceptions. For example, football is a sport requiring a modicum of aerobic fitness, with major emphasis being placed on explosive power. Offensive and defensive linemen in football need to be able to come off the line of scrimmage with explosive power. But—here is the key—they need to be able to do it time after time! The capacity to do so is called *strength endurance,* as discussed in Chapter 1.

Consequently, the system of choice for football linemen wishing to improve both power and endurance will be a *modified* version of the circuit training system described in Chapter 3. Squats, deadlifts, and bench presses will be done first, with a short rest between sets to allow for greater intensity on each set of these important football-related movements. Then the normal circuit training program is adhered to for the remainder of the exercises.

Similar alterations are generally built into weight-training programs for most sports that have both aerobic and anaerobic requirements. The purely anaerobic sports (such as shot putting, sprinting, etc.) have training programs quite different from those for the purely aerobic sports. The purely aerobic sports most generally will follow the systems described in Chapter 3. Sports that have both aerobic and anaerobic requirements will most frequently mix systems in such a way that the needs of the athlete are met. This is accomplished in a manner similar to the example for football players cited above.

The need to treat each athlete in every sport as an *individual* cannot be stressed too strongly. Each athlete will have his or her own goals, weaknesses, strengths, and lifestyle considerations. Constructing a weight-training program for any athlete must be a totally unique experience for that athlete or the coach. Because of the constraints related to individuality, the training programs listed in this chapter are meant to be starting points—guides—for athletes. As you go along, you will most certainly need to modify your program from time to time to align it more closely with your sport needs and especially with your position in your yearly cycle.

The rule of thumb for athletes approaching the competitive season is simply this: increase intensity and increase skill training. In-season training with weights generally will require fewer workouts per week, but the intensity of each workout should remain very high throughout the season. This is so the hard-won gains made during the off-season and preseason periods will not diminish throughout the competitive season.

Chapter 6 discusses self-assessment techniques that athletes can use in determining aerobic and anaerobic fitness levels. Another basic rule of thumb in constructing a training program for sports is first to determine your weaknesses and then to train them. Almost invariably when an athlete loses it is because of the presence of one or more weaknesses. Evaluating your fitness level in various tasks will give you an objective set of data from which you can establish training criteria and goals.

The final chapter deals with diet and nutrition. The nutritional requirements of an endurance athlete are not the same as those of other athletes. This is particularly true for precontest nutritional

FIGURE 5-1. Modified Circuit Training Program for Football Linemen

Warm-up should include all joints of the body.

1. Squats: Four or five sets of about eight reps done explosively (rest three to five minutes between sets).
2. Bench presses: Four or five sets of about eight reps done explosively (rest three to five minutes between sets).
3. High pulls: Four or five sets of about eight reps done explosively (rest three to five minutes between sets).
4. Proceed to the following circuit after these power exercises have been completed. Be sure to adhere to the target time the time it takes to complete the entire circuit from start to finish for the following circuit. Minimum heart rate is 140–150 BPM.

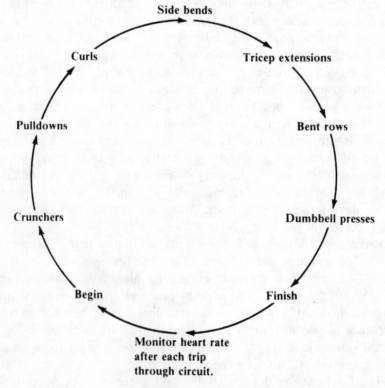

5. Each exercise in the circuit should be done with as much weight as possible for about 18–20 repetitions. Athletes should attempt to make at least three trips through the circuit.

requirements but is also true for general yearly training. Both Chapter 6 and Chapter 7 will be of benefit to you in establishing your weight-training program for the year.

Figures 5–1 through 5–8 illustrate weight-training programs for football (linemen), soccer, wrestling, cross-country skiing, long-distance swimming, long-distance running, basketball, and racquet sports.

FIGURE 5–2. PHA Weight Training Program for Soccer Players*

Sequence 1	Sequence 2	Sequence 3	Sequence 4
Squats	Leg curls	Leg pulleys	Toe Raises
Dumbbell presses	Lat pulldowns	Side bends	Lateral raises
Crunchers	High pulls	Curls	Tricep extensions

1. Do about 20 reps of squats with a weight that is equivalent to about 70 percent of your maximum.
2. Without resting, go on to dumbbell presses in like fashion and then on to crunchers, maintaining a heart rate of about 150 beats per minute throughout.
3. Repeat the exercises in Sequence 1 three or four times, resting at the completion of these sets until your heart rate is back to about 120 beats per minute. Then go on to Sequence 2, rest, proceed to Sequence 3, rest, and finish up with Sequence 4.
4. For increased power or strength, use more weight and fewer reps and do all movements with controlled explosiveness.
5. For increased cardiovascular endurance, use lighter weights for higher reps and minimize rest intervals while maximizing speed through each sequence, thereby maintaining as high a heart rate as tolerable without undue fatigue limiting training intensity.

* Each sport and each individual has different requirements. Therefore, each athlete must carefully select those exercises and training methods that will maximize goal attainment.

FIGURE 5–3. Circuit Training Program for Wrestlers

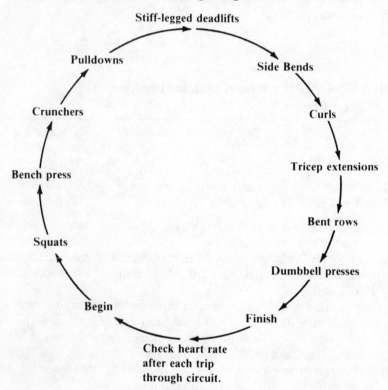

*Because the requirements of various sports differ from one another, the exercises in the circuit may be different for different sports. In fact, the exercises may vary within each sport, depending on the athlete's level of fitness, his or her position in the yearly cycle, and other factors.

FIGURE 5-4. A Parcourse Weight-Training Program for Cross-Country Skiers*

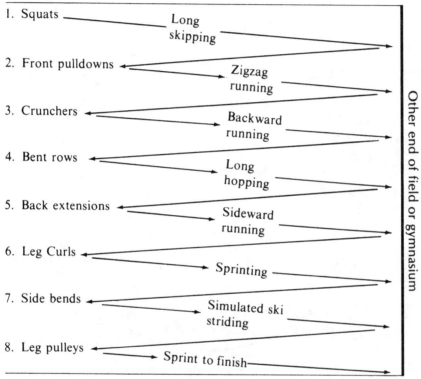

*The weight-training equipment is located at one end of the field or gym. The various methods of traversing the field or gym and to the weight-training equipment are designed to provide the skier with all forms of movement suited to simulating the varied terrain and movements encountered in cross-country skiing. The parcourse should be repeated at least three times in succession, maintaining a training heart rate of approximately 150 beats per minute.

FIGURE 5-5. Circuit Training Program for Long-Distance Swimmers

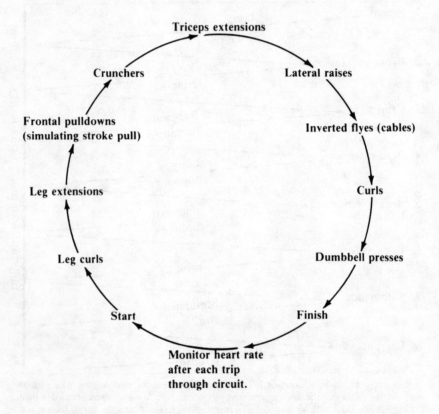

Note: Athletes should traverse circuit at least three times; around 25-30 reps per exercise should be done with a weight approximately equivalent to 60-70 percent of maximum.

FIGURE 5-6. An Interval Training Program with Weights for Long-Distance Runners

Exercise	Approx. Heart Rate	Approx. No. Reps.	Approx. Time
1. LUNGES (both legs)	150–165	25–30	60–90 sec
2. rest (active)	120		1–2 min
3. repeat 1 & 2 three times			
4. CRUNCHERS	150–165	25–30	60–90 sec
5. rest (active)	120		1–2 min
6. repeat 4 & 5 three times			
7. LEG CURLS	150–165	25–30	60–90 sec
8. active rest	120		1–2 min
9. repeat 7 & 8 three times			
10. PULLOVERS	150–165	25–30	60–90 sec
11. active rest	120		1–2 min
12. repeat 10 & 11 three times			
13. UPRIGHT ROWS	150–165	25–30	60–90 sec
14. active rest	120		1–2 min
15. repeat 13 & 14 three times			
16. TOE RAISES	150–165	25–30	60–90 sec
17. active rest	120		1–2 min
18. repeat 16 & 17 three times			
19. workout finished			

Note: It's easier to achieve the target heart rate when using the larger muscle(s). While exercising smaller muscles, don't worry if the target heart rate is not achieved; simply try to work as fast as possible without losing control of your movements with the weights.

Walk around or skip rope during the active rest periods.

Because of the possible trauma to knees and hips when running after weight training, it is always advisable to run before weight training—never after.

FIGURE 5-7. Interval Weight Training Program for Basketball*

Exercise	Approximate Heart Rate	Approximate Number of Reps	Approximate Time (minutes)
1. Warm-up and stretching	—	—	4-5
2. Squats and toe raises	150	20	1
3. Rest	120	—	1-3
4. Repeat 2 & 3 about 3 more times			
5. Bench press	150	20	1
6. Rest	120	—	1-3
7. Repeat 5 & 6 about 3 more times			
8. Crunchers	150	20	1
9. Rest	120	—	1-3
10. Repeat 8 & 9 about 3 more times			
11. Dumbbell presses	150	20	1
12. Rest	120	—	1-3
13. Repeat 11 & 12 about 3 more times			
14. Curls	150	20	1
15. Rest	120	—	1-3
16. Repeat 14 & 15 about 3 more times			
17. Hamstring curls	150	20	1
18. Rest	150	20	1-3
19. Repeat 17 & 18 about 3 more times—workout finished			

* Because the requirements of individuals or sports generally vary, the exercises described here may vary as well. Each athlete in every sport should take his or her sport requirements into consideration when constructing a conditioning program.

FIGURE 5-8. Parcourse Weight-Training Program for Racquet Sports

1. Crunchers ⸻⟶ Long skipping ⸻

2. Lunges ⟵⸻ Zigzag running ⸻

3. Leg curls ⟵⸻ Backward running ⸻

4. Bench presses (dumbbells) ⟵⸻ Long hopping ⸻

5. Inverted flyes (cables) ⟵⸻ Sideward running ⸻

6. Side bends left and right ⟵⸻ Sprinting ⸻

7. Frontal pulldowns ⟵⸻ Hops with a half-twist ⸻

8. Tricep extensions ⟵⸻ Very long jumps ⸻

9. High pulls ⟵⸻ Jog ⸻

10. Workout finish ⟵⸻

Note: The weight-training program is located at one end of the gym or field. The various methods of crossing the open area are designed to allow the athlete the opportunity of simulating the many types of movement patterns that are common to racquet sports play. In the absence of a large gym or field, these movement patterns can be simulated within a very small or confined area by doing them in place (as in running in place).

6

Self-Assessment
Techniques for Sports
Fitness

INTRODUCTION

One of the most important attributes of a good coach is the ability to detect weaknesses in athletes' performance or conditioning. Once identified, those weaknesses are relatively simple to eliminate. Fitness enthusiasts and athletes training alone must also develop means by which they can objectively view their level of conditioning. That the elimination of weaknesses in one's performance or conditioning will lead to increased performance capabilities is common sense.

Common sense has an eerie way of being scarce, however. For example, the athlete who detects a weakness in his legs' muscular endurance will, in commonsense fashion, set out to eliminate that weakness. Once eliminated, what comes next? The fact that there will always be an aspect of conditioning or performance that stands out as a weakness goes unconsidered more often than not. As weaknesses are eliminated, other weaknesses will become evident and will beg for treatment, making training a never-ending process.

This chapter is devoted to establishing easy-to-use methods of detecting weaknesses in aerobic capacity, either cardiovascular or muscular. The exact test(s) chosen will be determined by the athlete's or coach's perception of what is important.

MEASURING AEROBIC CAPACITY

In Chapter 1 it was pointed out that aerobic capacity is largely a function of one's ability to utilize oxygen. The amount of oxygen one consumes is traditionally measured in milliliters of oxygen consumed per kilogram of body weight in one minute. The following chart, adapted from Cooper's book, *The New Aerobics,* serves as a guide for determining one's aerobic fitness. It goes without saying that an athlete's oxygen consumption capabilities average considerably higher than the normal person's. Therefore, any endurance athlete's fitness index should fall into the good-to-excellent range.

Thus, for an athlete under 30 years old weighing 154 pounds (69.85 kilograms), the total amount of oxygen consumed in one minute, provided his category rating is excellent, would be 3,604.26 milliliters (69.85 × 51.6).

FIGURE 6-1. Cooper's Aerobic Fitness Categories for Men

Category	Oxygen Consumption (max VO₂ uptake—ml/kg/min)			
	under 30	*30–39*	*40–49*	*over 50*
Very poor	under 25	under 25	under 25	____
Below average	25–33.7	25–30.1	25–26.4	under 25
Average	33.8–42.5	30.2–39.1	26.5–35.4	25–33.7
Above average	42.6–51.5	39.2–48	35.5–45	33.8–43
Excellent	+ 51.6	+ 48.1	+ 45.1	+ 43.1

Cooper's 12-Minute Test

Perhaps the easiest way to determine how much oxygen is being consumed is to use Cooper's 12-minute test. In laboratory studies Cooper found that the distance covered in 12 minutes of running and/or walking was very highly correlated with measurements derived from the use of highly sophisticated and expensive laboratory equipment. The person being tested simply covers as much distance as possible in 12 minutes, and that distance is then applied to a chart listing approximate oxygen consumption levels. Figure 6-2 is an adapted version of Cooper's research findings.

FIGURE 6–2. Distance Covered in 12 Minutes and Corresponding Oxygen Consumption Values

Miles Traveled in 12 Minutes	Oxygen Consumed (ml/kg/min)
under 1 mile	under 25
up to 1 ¼ miles	25–33.7
up to 1 ½ miles	33.8–42.5
up to 1 ¾ miles	42.6–51.5
over 1 ¾ miles	more than 51.6

For generally fit athletes, engaging in such a test is probably safe. However, if you are over 30 years old or you are an unfit individual, Cooper recommends that you have a thorough physical examination and/or engage in a starter program designed to make you fit enough to take the test.

The Harvard Step Test

Another easy-to-administer test of cardiovascular fitness is a test devised some years ago at Harvard University. The test simply requires stepping up and down on a stable bench at least 15 inches in height (i.e., knee height). The step-ups are done at a rate of one per second and should last for up to five minutes in order to reach a stable heart rate. If you have a metronome, timing the rate of step-ups will be easier.

After completing the step-ups the athlete sits quietly for one minute and then measures his or her pulse rate. The easiest way to measure pulse rate is to place the fingers over the carotid artery (on the right side of your throat), and count the number of beats for 30 seconds. Then multiply that figure by two to derive a heart rate (per minute) figure. Locate your pulse rate for 30 seconds on Figure 6–3 to determine your aerobic fitness score.

The score you achieve should be interpreted as follows:

Below 50....................... Poor aerobic fitness

Between 50 and 80 .... Average aerobic fitness

Above 80 .... Good aerobic fitness

Needless to say, any endurance athlete should score at least 70—probably higher—to be considered in good condition for his or her respective sport.

FIGURE 6-3. Harvard Step Test Scoring Table*

Duration of Effort	Heartbeats for 30 seconds from 1 to 1½ min after exercise										
	40–44	45–49	50–54	55–59	60–64	65–69	70–74	75–79	80–84	85–89	90–over
1–1½ min.	30	30	25	25	20	20	20	20	15	15	15
1½–2 min.	45	40	40	35	30	30	25	25	25	20	20
2–2½ min.	60	50	45	45	40	35	35	30	30	30	25
2½–3 min.	70	65	60	55	50	45	40	40	35	35	35
3–3½ min.	85	75	70	60	55	55	50	45	45	40	40
3½–4 min.	100	85	80	70	65	60	55	55	50	45	45
4–4½ min.	110	100	90	80	75	70	65	60	55	55	50
4½–4'59"	125	110	100	90	85	75	70	65	60	60	55
5 min.	130	115	105	95	90	80	75	70	65	65	60

* Adapted from Krotee, M., and Hatfield, F. C., *Theory and Practice of Physical Activity* (Dubuque: Kendall/Hunt Publishing Co., 1979), p. 30.

MEASURING LOCAL MUSCULAR ENDURANCE

Many sophisticated laboratory techniques have been developed to measure decrements in a given muscle's strength level as fatigue sets in. However, to judge an athlete's initial muscular endurance and then retest over time (in order to determine whether there is a significant training effect), much simpler methods have been developed that require no laboratory equipment.

As discussed in Chapter 1, two types of measurements are used in determining local muscular endurance. One is called *absolute endurance* and describes the actual endurance of any person's muscle in comparison to anyone else's. To do this, simply have all of the athletes being tested hold a weight with the muscle being tested. Each person holds the *same amount* of weight. Then that muscle's absolute endurance is recorded as the length of time the weight is held. In this way it is easy to compare athletes in absolute terms.

Absolute endurance is highly related to muscle strength. The person with the strongest muscle will almost always be the person with the greatest absolute endurance. In order to test one's *relative endurance,* however, simply have each athlete hold a weight that is equivalent to a given percentage of his or her own body weight. By doing so, *strength* no longer becomes a factor, and the *aerobic* efficiency of the muscle will be tested more accurately.

MEASURING PERCENTAGE OF BODY FAT

Because fat does little in the way of contributing to athletic performance, having as little of it as possible is generally considered wise. This is especially true for endurance athletes who need to be able to minimize the excess baggage that has to be carried around. It is also critical that athletes required to compete in various weight divisions (e.g., boxing or wrestling) have as little fat as possible and as much muscle as possible in order to improve their efficiency within the confines of the weight division they're competing in.

For these reasons, it is important to monitor your percentage of body fat at least two or three times monthly. Your training efforts and strict dieting must pay off, and the best way to determine this is through objective means. If your percentage of body fat is too high and climbing, you are obviously negligent in your training, in your diet, or in both.

The majority of medical doctors generally agree that the following guidelines are appropriate when considering each person's percentage of body fat.

FIGURE 6-4. Clinical Classifications for Percentages of Body Fat—Recommended or Clinical

Percentage of Body Fat		Classification
1–10		Male athletes
10–14	Recommended	Female athletes
10–14		Average adult male
14–18		Average adult female
20–22		Clinical obesity—men
25–28	Clinical	Clinical obesity—women
28–30		Chronic obesity—men
35–38		Chronic obesity—women

There are a number of highly accurate methods of measuring one's body fat level, including such laboratory techniques as X-ray, hydrostatic weighing (through the use of Archimedes' principle, which shows how much your body weighs when compared to an equal volume of water), and many others. For the practicing athlete or fitness enthusiast, however, there are some rather easy methods that require nothing more than a tape measure and a weight scale. The two presented in Figures 6-5 and 6-6 are for men and women, respectively. They are among the simplest to administer and have a very low error factor, varying as little as a percentage point or two from one's actual percentage of body fat. The techniques will be quite accurate if administered in exactly the same way each time a reading is taken.

FIGURE 6–5. Estimating Percentage of Body Fat for Men

Fat-free weight = 94.42 + (1.082 × nude body weight in pounds)
$\qquad$ − (4.15 × waist girth at umbilicus)

Example: 94.42 + (1.082 × 154 lbs.) − (4.15 × 29 inches) =
$\qquad$ 94.42 + 166.628 − 120.35 = 140.70 pounds

Thus, the 154-pound man in this example would weigh 140.7 pounds if all of his fat were removed from his body.

Then, to determine the percentage of his total body weight that is comprised of fat, divide the difference (13.3 pounds) by his total body weight (154 pounds).

$\qquad$ % body fat = 13.3 divided by 154 = 8.64 %

FIGURE 6–6. Estimating Percentage of Body Fat for Women

Lean body weight = 8.987 + 0.732 (body weight$_{kg}$)
$\qquad$ + 3.786 (wrist diameter$_{cm}$)
$\qquad$ − 0.157 (abdominal circumference$_{cm}$)
$\qquad$ − 0.249 (hip circumference$_{cm}$)
$\qquad$ + 0.434 (forearm circumference$_{cm}$)

Example: A woman weighing 50 kilograms with a wrist diameter (distance across the top of the wrist) of 6 centimeters has an abdominal circumference (distance around the midsection, positioning the tape across the belly button) of 70 centimeters, a hip circumference (distance around the hips, positioning the tape at the widest point) of 95 centimeters, and a forearm circumference (distance around the forearm at its widest point) of 22 centimeters.

LBW = 8.987 + 0.732 (50) + 3.786 (6) − 0.157 (70) − 0.249 (95)
$\qquad$ + 0.434 (22)
$\qquad$ = 8.987 + 36.6 + 22.716 − 10.99 − 23.655 + 9.548
$\qquad$ = 43.206 kilograms (95¼ pounds)

Thus, our 50-kilogram (110¼-pound) woman would weigh only 43.206 kilograms (95¼ pounds) if all of her fat were removed.

Then, to determine the percentage of her total body weight that is comprised of fat, divide the difference (15 pounds) by her total body weight (110¼ pounds).

$\qquad$ % body fat = 15 divided by 110.25 = 13.61 %

Note: one kilogram is equivalent to 2.2046 pounds.

7

Nutrition for the Endurance Athlete

INTRODUCTION

The science of nutrition is still in its infancy, but there are nonetheless a number of facts from which any athlete can profit. Nutrition is perhaps the most controversial of all topics in the world of sports and fitness, and the average athlete, taken to excesses, has fallen prey to all sorts of faddists and soothsayers claiming to have the answer to all nutritional needs.

So, with the ever-growing number of facts about nutrition that there are available, most of the food fads of the '70s have passed by the board. Still, many athletes cling to their belief in ritualistic pregame eating habits and in megadoses of vitamins and minerals. Many still gorge themselves on protein powder and brewer's yeast, liver pills and bee pollen, wheat germ and black strap molasses. The list of fad foods is nearly endless.

The best available evidence indicates that at least three meals per day (preferably four or even five) comprised of foods from each of the four basic food groups will provide exceptional nutrition for any athlete or nonathlete. Most nutritionists pooh-pooh the notion that soil depletion, food processing, and additives in foods have rendered the average American's daily diet inadequate. Yet, nutritionists, exercise physiologists, and medical

99

doctors from many quarters of the country continue to present what they claim is evidence supporting the notion that supplementing one's daily intake of food is beneficial, particularly for the competing athlete in heavy training. Of course, the most common supplements mentioned are vitamin and mineral pills and protein.

There is also widespread belief in the notion that athletes from various sports can benefit (in terms of performance) from a carefully planned pregame diet, the contents of which are reported to vary from sport to sport.

In spite of all of the claims and counterclaims regarding what constitutes maximally beneficial nutrition for the serious athlete, certain facts must be taken into account by any athlete wishing to maximize the benefit derived from what is eaten. Sticking to these basic facts concerning nutrition, and thereby avoiding the faddist approach, will probably allow any athlete to progress to performance levels at least equal to that achieved through any of a number of exotic diet plans.

CALORIES

A calorie is a measure of heat. The amount of heat that is required to raise the temperature of one gram of water one degree centigrade equals one calorie. The caloric value of food is measured by how much heat that food can produce when burned. The food we eat is ultimately converted to fat or glycogen and stored as adipose tissue (fat) or in the liver and muscles (glycogen). All bodily functions require energy (including physical activity), and the fat and glycogen are used to produce this energy. Enzymes in the muscles are produced in the cells' mitochondria (spoken of in Chapter 1). These enzymes effect the utilization of the stored glycogen for use as energy fuel.

The specific speed at which these calories are expended during rest (i.e., lying in bed awake) is called the *basal metabolic rate* (BMR). One's BMR is affected by sex, age, body size (both surface area and total weight), physical condition, and endocrine function. The average BMR for a 20-year-old man is approximately equal to one calorie per kilogram of body weight for a 24-

hour period. For the average 20-year-old woman, it is approximately 0.9 calorie per kilogram of body weight for the same period of time. For example, a 20-year-old man weighing 154 pounds will, on the average, expend approximately 1,680 calories at a basal rate (154 divided by 2.2 times 24). A woman of the same size will expend approximately 1,512 calories in the same 24-hour period (154 divided by 2.2 times 0.9 times 24).

FIGURE 7–1. Average BMR for Men and Women

Men's BMR (Basal Metabolic Rate) = $1 \times \text{body weight}_{kg} \times 24$
Women's BMR = $0.9 \times \text{body weight}_{kg} \times 24$

Athletes older than 20 will, due to a relatively lower BMR, use fewer calories per day, but the difference is probably minimal if we can assume that older athletes' activity levels are equivalent to that of the average 20-year-old athlete's.

Many charts and graphs have been generated over the years that illustrate how many calories are expended when engaging in various types of sports and activities. The true significance of such charts is not in assisting the user in choosing an activity, but rather in computing caloric expenditure levels throughout the day and thereby controlling food intake. This, in turn, will allow the athlete to control his or her percentage of body fat or overall body weight.

One such chart is presented in Figure 7–2. It has the advantage of being applicable to a wide variety of activities since it is computed on the basis of both body weight and heart rate, as well as sex.

To understand the significance of the preceding table, let's take a look at the following example of a 181-pound athlete engaging in a one-hour workout with weights. The example athlete performed five sets of five reps in each of his exercises, with about five minutes of rest between sets.

FIGURE 7-2. Approximate KCalories per Minute Expanded per Body Weight and Heart Rate for Men and Women*

Body Weight	Sex	Heart Rate			
		100	*125*	*150*	*175*
100	M	2.75	5.75	8.75	11.75
	F	2.48	5.18	7.88	10.58
114	M	3.75	6.75	9.75	12.75
	F	3.38	6.08	8.78	11.48
123	M	4.0	7.0	10.0	13.0
	F	3.6	6.3	9.0	11.7
132	M	4.5	7.5	10.5	13.5
	F	4.1	6.75	9.45	12.15
148	M	5.0	8.0	11.0	14.0
	F	4.5	7.2	9.9	12.6
165	M	5.5	8.5	11.5	14.5
	F	5.0	7.65	10.35	13.05
181	M	6.0	9.0	12.0	15.0
	F	5.4	8.1	10.8	13.5
198	M	6.5	9.5	12.5	15.5
	F	5.9	8.55	11.25	13.95
220	M	7.25	10.25	13.25	16.25
242	M	8.0	11.0	14.0	17.0
275	M	9.0	12.0	15.0	18.0
300	M	10.0	13.0	16.0	19.0
325	M	11.0	14.0	17.0	20.0

* Taken from Hatfield, F. C., *The Complete Guide to Power Training,* Fitness Systems (New Orleans), 1982. Used by permission.

```
Time per set........................... 2 minutes
Average HR during set .................. 150 BPM
Average HR during recovery
    1st minute .......................... 125 BPM
    2nd minute........................... 110 BPM
    3rd minute .......................... 100 BPM
    4th minute .......................... 98 BPM
    5th minute .......................... 96 BPM
Average for 7-minute period............. 118.43 BPM
Average HR for entire hour ............. 118.43 BPM
```

Through simple interpolation we can determine the approximate number of calories expended during the hour-long workout:

```
Calories expended during set .................. 24.00
Calories expended during recovery
    1st minute .................................. 9.00
    2nd minute................................... 6.83
    3rd minute .................................. 6.00
    4th minute .................................. 5.80
    5th minute .................................. 5.60
Average caloric expenditure for 7 minutes....... 57.23
Average caloric requirement for 1 hour ........ 490.54
```

Compare this figure with the number of calories the same athlete would expend running at a pace of one mile every 7 minutes for one hour. He would expend about 1,000 calories. If we were to assume that our example athlete expended 1,980 calories at a basal level during each 24-hour period, we could calculate with a fair degree of accuracy the number of calories used over a normal day. The figures might look something like this:

```
Sleeping 8 hours .............................. 800
1 hour workout with weights ................... 490
1 hour run at 7 min/mile pace ................. 1,000
14 hours general activity ..................... 2,100
            Total Daily Calories spent = 4,390
```

Reference to Figure 7–3 may assist you in deriving a more accurate assessment of your caloric requirements for various activities throughout the day. The figures listed are for a 154-pound male athlete. To derive a more accurate figure for your own body weight, simply add or subtract 10 KCalories per hour per activity for each five pounds your own body weight deviates from the 154-pound standard used. Remember that age, sex, body area, and body weight will make your actual caloric expenditure vary, and the figure you derive will only be an estimate.

FIGURE 7–3. Average Caloric Expenditure for a 154-Pound Man during One Hour of Selected Activities*

Activity	Estimated Kcal/Hour
badminton	400
basketball	560
billiards	235
bowling	215
bull session	90
calisthenics	200
cleaning	185
cycling (easy pace)	300
disco	450
driving a car	180
golf	340
lying quietly (awake)	80
playing cards	140
racquet sports	870
running (7-minute mile)	950
sitting in class	90
studying/reading	105
swimming (steady pace)	500
walking (normal pace)	180
sleeping	70
walking up stairs	300

* Adapted from Krotee, M., and Hatfield, F. C., *Theory and Practice of Physical Activity* (Dubuque: Kendall/Hunt Publishing Co., 1979), p. 67.

WEIGHT CONTROL

Fats, carbohydrates, and protein are the three sources of calories in our diets. Figure 7-4 illustrates the differential rate at which each is utilized as energy fuel.

FIGURE 7-4. KCalories Derived from One Gram of Fats, Carbohydrates, or Protein

Calorie Source	Energy Required to Burn One Gram of the Respective Sources
fats	9.45 Kcal
carbohydrates	4.10 Kcal
protein	5.65 Kcal

It becomes immediately clear that fat constitutes a very concentrated form of energy, with carbohydrates being the lowest. Yet carbohydrates are most easily converted to glycogen in the body, making it the best energy source of the three. To state the table figures another way, perhaps a more useful way: every 3,500 calories one consumes above his or her required amount will result in one pound of fat being stored. This means that you can get fatter by one pound through ingesting 370.37 grams of fat, 853.66 grams of carbohydrates, or 619.47 grams of protein above what you would need to maintain your normal body weight.

Gaining Weight

No self-respecting athlete wishing to gain weight would opt to gain it from increased fat. To avoid putting on fat during the weight gain process, two factors are of vital importance: (1) you must restrict your caloric intake to no more than 500 calories above your daily requirement, and (2) you must train with weights. It is only through these two procedures that gained weight will be muscle. There is no other way known to science to gain muscle weight (even muscle-producing drugs like somatotropic hormones and anabolic steroids will not work without increased caloric intake and weight training).

By increasing one's caloric intake by a factor of 500 calories per day, and weight training on a regular schedule, an athlete can expect to gain about 1 pound of muscle per week under optimal conditions. It will rarely be more than that, and more often it will be less. So the secret is to find the rate at which you, individually, can put on muscle without allowing your percentage of body fat to increase and to control your caloric intake accordingly. You may find it helpful to be lazy throughout the day, limiting your activity to workouts only. This will reduce your caloric requirement as well as your basal metabolism—you'll burn fewer calories.

Losing Weight

The keys to gaining weight were to train with weights and generate a positive caloric balance in the body. To lose weight, you must maintain a negative caloric balance. By taking in 500 calories per day fewer than required to maintain your present weight, you will lose about one pound per week. However, research has clearly indicated that the body, being quite conservative, will claim needed calories from the most accessible stores. The most accessible stores happen to be muscle tissue, not fat. So, again weight training becomes extremely important in maintaining a good level of lean body weight. The increased stress on the muscles resulting from weight training will ensure the integrity of the muscle tissue, and the calories required will be reclaimed from fat stores instead.

Generally, sport activities, including running, do not constitute sufficient stress on the general musculature to allow them to grow. The most efficient way is through weight training, using the systems described in Chapter 3.

What to Eat

The four food groups are (1) the meat and egg group, (2) the dairy group, (3) the vegetable and fruit group, and (4) the grain and cereal group. Each of these groups of foods has fats, carbohydrates, and protein in varying ratios. Most nutritionists agree that if one's three to five meals per day are comprised of a variety of foods from each food group, one's nutritional requirements in terms of vitamins, minerals, fats, carbohydrates, protein, and fiber will be adequate. That, according to many, is a very big *if.*

On the other hand, it has been established fairly well that "megadosing" on so-called health foods and scores of vitamin and mineral pills is not only superfluous but often dangerous. Probably appropriate, however, is to use a good brand of multivitamin/ mineral tablet each day (for insurance) and to eat as soundly as possible.

Athletes in heavy training are well advised to attempt to limit the ratio of fats, carbohydrates, and protein intake to the following proportions:

Fats . . . . 15–20 percent of daily caloric intake
Carbohydrates . . . . 50–60 percent of daily caloric intake
Protein . . . . 20–25 percent of daily caloric intake

Some sources of information may vary a bit from these recommended percentages, but for the athlete in heavy training these are probably quite sufficient, particularly if one's food is derived from wholesome, fresh sources. Purchase a small pocket calorie counter guide, and in a few weeks it will become almost automatic for you to establish sound eating habits at each meal.

How to Eat

On a day-to-day basis during the off-season training period, three to five meals per day are recommended. There are a number of good reasons for this schedule. First, if your body has a constant supply of energy coming in on a frequent basis, it never needs to develop the capacity to store energy in the form of fat. The fat-storing enzymes never appear, and fat never gets stored. Regulating the number of calories at each meal, however, is a must. Try to make each meal throughout the day equal in size (caloric value) and the total caloric value equivalent to your daily requirement. (Caloric intake should be slightly higher if you're trying to gain muscle weight and slightly lower if you're trying to lose fat weight.)

Don't snack between meals. It takes roughly four hours for food to digest and for the assimilation process to begin. Food ingested during the digestive process will tend to disrupt the process and sometimes can result in incomplete digestion and assimilation. Food sitting in the warm confines of one's intestines will rot and produce all sorts of toxins that may ultimately hinder performance or progress.

THE PREGAME MEAL

Many long-distance athletes now use a system of eating during the last few days before a contest called *glycogen supercompensation* or *carbohydrate loading*. Not to be used more than two or three times per year, this system of eating is said to result in increased endurance capacity. The mechanism underlying this increased endurance capacity is the increased supply of glycogen in the muscles' cells. Glycogen, you will recall, is an end product of the food you ingest and is a major source of the body's energy. Figure 7–5 illustrates how many athletes gain increased muscle glycogen stores.

FIGURE 7–5. Glycogen Supercompensation Schedule Typically Used by Endurance Athletes

Phase 1: The Depletion Stage
   Seven days before competition: exhausting exercise
   Six days before competition: low carbohydrate diet
                               (high fat and protein)
   Five days before competition: low carbohydrate diet
                               (high fat and protein)
   Four days before competition: low carbohydrate diet
                               (high fat and protein)
Phase 2: The Supercompensation Phase
   Three days before competition: high carbohydrate diet
                               (normal fat and protein)
   Two days before competition: high carbohydrate diet
                               (normal fat and protein)
   One day before competition: high carbohydrate diet
                               (normal fat and protein)
Phase 3: Competition

Another way of expressing the above schedule is in terms of the percentages of fats, carbohydrates, and protein that the meals during each of the seven days should consist of. Thus, Phase 1 meals might look like this:

Fat = 45–50 percent
Protein = 45–50 percent
Carbohydrates = 0–10 percent

Phase 2 meals may look like this:

Fat = 15 percent
Protein = 15 percent
Carbohydrates = 70 percent

During Phase 1 the initial step is to deplete one's glycogen stores as much as possible with an exhausting bout of exercise (usually running as much as 15–20 miles). Then further deplete the body's stores of glycogen by eating below-normal levels of carbohydrate foods. Then, during Phase 2, the athlete packs in as much carbohydrate food as possible, thereby replenishing the stores of glycogen. Because the body has a tendency to overcompensate for stress (the low-carbohydrate phase was stressful to the body), greater-than-normal levels of glycogen are stored in the muscles. With increased stores of glycogen the endurance athlete experiences fatigue later in the endurance event.

A great majority of athletes engaged in aerobic sports, however, never need to follow such a drastic diet plan. Football players are known for their insistence on a thick steak before games. Other athletes may eat only a salad, while others fill up with sugar and sweets. Many of these athletes go on to break world records or set standards of excellence in their respective sports that are truly amazing. The vast array of strange and often ritualistic eating habits most probably accounts for very little of these athletes' top performance capabilities. And they probably don't detract from them very much either.

Still, most athletes choose to follow their own peculiar eating pattern prior to competing. This is probably as it should be, considering the fact that of all the pregame detractors, *tension* probably has the most devastating effect on performance. Eating normally may reduce the tension often felt by athletes who, because of the game, alter normal lifestyle patterns.

Still, looking at things a bit more scientifically, there appears to be a few tips on how an athlete should eat prior to competition. Dr. Nathan Smith, writing in *The Journal of the American Medical Association,* states that athletes should stay away from salty foods such as:

table salt	monosodium glutamate
sauerkraut	potato chips
pretzels	other salty snacks
mustard	relish and pickles
soy sauce	instant cocoa mix
Worcestershire sauce	dry cereals
sausage	catsup
sardines	bouillon cubes
cheese	peanut butter
canned soups	

Dr. Smith further states that high-fiber foods are not recommended for athletes prior to competing. He lists such foods as:

raw fruits and vegetables
salads
dried fruits
nuts
whole-grain cereals or breads
berry or fruit pies

He also recommends against eating milk or cheese within 24 hours of a game or competition.

Figure 7-6 lists the kinds of considerations any athlete should take into account in choosing an appropriate pregame eating schedule. The fact is, that with a few simple and commonsense exceptions, the fewer deviations from your normal eating habits you make prior to a game or meet, the better off you'll probably be.

FIGURE 7-6. General Suggestions Regarding Pregame Meals

1. Energy intake should be sufficient to ward off hunger throughout the meet or game.

2. The diet plan should allow enough time for emptying of the stomach and upper gastrointestinal tract prior to weigh-in or the game.

3. Fluid intake should be sufficient (both before and during competition) to ensure adequate fluid replacement from sweating or dropping weight for weigh-in.

4. Avoid irritating foods such as beans, spicy foods, or foods that you are not accustomed to.

5. Avoid high-fiber foods and high-protein foods just prior to competition, as they are not digested or absorbed quickly.

6. A bland, nongreasy meal such as pancakes, pasta, or liquid meals is generally recommended as the pregame meal.

7. Avoid simple sugars prior to a contest, as they result in a hyperglycemic state and also delay the absorption of liquids by the tissue.

8. During the contest, fluids drunk for replacement of sweat should be cool water or cool diluted commercial drinks such as Gatorade, etc.

Index